GREAT ASTRONOMERS

BY

Sir ROBERT S. BALL, D.Sc., LL.D., F.R.S.

LOWDEAN PROFESSOR OF ASTRONOMY AND GEOMETRY AT THE
UNIVERSITY OF CAMBRIDGE.

NEW WEST PRESS

Ordering Information:
Special discounts are available on quantity purchases by corporations, associations, educators, and others. For details, contact the publisher at the listed address below.

U.S. trade bookstores and wholesalers: Please contact New West Press:

email: contact@nwwst.com

PREFACE.

It has been my object in these pages to present the life of each astronomer in such detail as to enable the reader to realise in some degree the man's character and surroundings; and I have endeavoured to indicate as clearly as circumstances would permit the main features of the discoveries by which he has become known.

There are many types of astronomers—from the stargazer who merely watches the heavens, to the abstract mathematician who merely works at his desk; it has, consequently, been necessary in the case of some lives to adopt a very different treatment from that which seemed suitable for others.

While the work was in progress, some of the sketches appeared in *Good Words.* The chapter on Brinkley has been chiefly derived from an article on the "History of Dunsink Observatory," which was published on the occasion of the tercentenary celebration of the University of Dublin in 1892, and the life of Sir William Rowan Hamilton is taken, with a few alterations and omissions, from an article contributed to the *Quarterly Review* on Graves' life of the great mathematician. The remaining chapters now appear for the first time. For many of the facts contained in the sketch of the late Professor Adams, I am indebted to the obituary notice written by my friend Dr. J. W. L. Glaisher, for the Royal Astronomical Society; while with regard to the late Sir George Airy, I have a similar acknowledgment to make to Professor H. H. Turner. To my friend Dr. Arthur A. Rambaut I owe my hearty thanks for his kindness in aiding me in the revision of the work.

R.S.B.

The Observatory, Cambridge.
October, 1895.

CONTENTS.

———◆———

GREENWICH OBSERVATORY.

INTRODUCTION.

Of all the natural sciences there is not one which offers such sublime objects to the attention of the inquirer as does the science of astronomy. From the earliest ages the study of the stars has exercised the same fascination as it possesses at the present day. Among the most primitive peoples, the movements of the sun, the moon, and the stars commanded attention from their supposed influence on human affairs.

The practical utilities of astronomy were also obvious in primeval times. Maxims of extreme antiquity show how the avocations of the husbandman are to be guided by the movements of the heavenly bodies. The positions of the stars indicated the time to plough, and the time to sow. To the mariner who was seeking a way across the trackless ocean, the heavenly bodies offered the only reliable marks by which his path could be guided. There was, accordingly, a stimulus both from intellectual curiosity and from practical necessity to follow the movements of the stars. Thus began a search for the causes of the ever-varying phenomena which the heavens display.

Many of the earliest discoveries are indeed prehistoric. The great diurnal movement of the heavens, and the annual revolution of the sun, seem to have been known in times far more ancient than those to which any human monuments can be referred. The acuteness of the early observers enabled them to single out the more important of the wanderers which we now call planets. They saw that the star-like objects, Jupiter, Saturn, and Mars, with the more conspicuous Venus, constituted a class of bodies wholly distinct from the fixed stars among which their movements lay, and to which they bear such a superficial resemblance. But the penetration of the early astronomers went even further, for they recognized that Mercury also belongs to the same group, though this particular object is seen so rarely. It would seem that eclipses and other phenomena were observed at Babylon from a very remote period, while the most ancient records of celestial observations that we possess are to be found in the Chinese annals.

The study of astronomy, in the sense in which we understand the word, may be said to have commenced under the reign of the Ptolemies at Alexandria. The most famous name in the science of this period is that of Hipparchus who lived and worked at Rhodes about the year 160BC. It was his splendid investigations that first wrought the observed facts into a coherent branch of knowledge. He recognized the primary obligation which lies on the student of the heavens to compile as complete an inventory as possible of the objects which are there to be found. Hipparchus accordingly commenced by undertaking, on a small scale, a task exactly similar to that on which modern astronomers, with all available appliances of meridian circles, and photographic telescopes, are constantly engaged at the present day. He compiled a catalogue of the principal fixed stars, which is of special value to astronomers, as being the earliest work of its kind which has been handed down. He also studied the movements of the sun and the moon, and framed theories to account for the incessant changes which he saw in progress. He found a much more difficult problem in his attempt to interpret satisfactorily the complicated movements of the planets. With the view of constructing a theory which should give some coherent account of the subject, he made many observations of the places of these wandering stars. How great were the advances which Hipparchus accomplished may be appreciated if we reflect that, as a preliminary task to his more purely astronomical labours, he had to invent that branch of mathematical science by which alone the problems he proposed could be solved. It was for this purpose that he devised the indispensable method of calculation which we now know so well as trigonometry. Without the aid rendered by this beautiful art it would have been impossible for any really important advance in astronomical calculation to have been effected.

But the discovery which shows, beyond all others, that Hipparchus possessed one of the master-minds of all time was the detection of that remarkable celestial movement known as the precession of the equinoxes. The inquiry which conducted to this discovery involved a most profound investigation, especially when it is remembered that in the days of Hipparchus the means of observation of the heavenly bodies were only of the rudest description, and the available observations of earlier dates were extremely scanty. We can but look with astonishment on the genius of the man who, in spite of such difficulties, was able to detect such a phenomenon as the precession, and to exhibit its actual magnitude. I shall endeavour to explain the nature of this singular celestial movement, for it may be said to offer the first instance in the history of science in which we find that combination of accurate observation with skilful interpretation, of which, in the subsequent development of astronomy, we have so many splendid examples.

The word equinox implies the condition that the night is equal to the day. To a resident on the equator the night is no doubt equal to the day at all times in the year, but to one who lives on any other part of the earth, in either hemisphere, the night and the day are not generally equal. There is, however, one occasion in spring, and another in autumn, on which the day and the night are each twelve hours at all places on the earth. When the night and day are equal in spring, the point which the sun occupies on the heavens is termed the vernal equinox. There is similarly another point in which the sun is situated at the time of the autumnal equinox. In any investigation of the celestial movements the positions of these two equinoxes on the heavens are of primary importance, and Hipparchus, with the instinct of genius, perceived their significance, and commenced to study them. It will be understood that we can always define the position of a point on the sky with reference to the surrounding stars. No doubt we do not see the stars near the sun when the sun is shining, but they are there nevertheless. The ingenuity of Hipparchus enabled him to determine the positions of each of the two equinoxes relatively to the stars which lie in its immediate vicinity. After examination of the celestial places of these points at different periods, he was led to the conclusion that each equinox was moving relatively to the stars, though that movement was so slow that twenty five thousand years would necessarily elapse before a complete circuit of the heavens was accomplished. Hipparchus traced out this phenomenon, and established it on an impregnable basis, so that all astronomers have ever since recognised the precession of the equinoxes as one of the fundamental facts of astronomy. Not until nearly two thousand years after Hipparchus had made this splendid discovery was the explanation of its cause given by Newton.

From the days of Hipparchus down to the present hour the science of astronomy has steadily grown. One great observer after another has appeared from time to time, to reveal some new phenomenon with regard to the celestial bodies or their movements, while from time to time one commanding intellect after another has arisen to explain the true import of the facts of observations. The history of astronomy thus becomes inseparable from the history of the great men to whose labours its development is due.

In the ensuing chapters we have endeavoured to sketch the lives and the work of the great philosophers, by whose labours the science of astronomy has been created. We shall commence with Ptolemy, who, after the foundations of the science had been laid by Hipparchus, gave to astronomy the form in which it was taught throughout the Middle Ages. We shall next see the mighty revolution in our conceptions of the universe which are associated with the name of Copernicus. We then pass to those periods illumined by the genius of Galileo and Newton, and afterwards we shall trace the careers of other more recent discoverers, by whose industry and genius the boundaries of human knowledge have been so greatly extended. Our history will be brought down late enough to include some of the illustrious astronomers who laboured in the generation which has just passed away.

PTOLEMY.

The career of the famous man whose name stands at the head of this chapter is one of the most remarkable in the history of human learning. There may have been other discoverers who have done more for science than ever Ptolemy accomplished, but there never has been any other discoverer whose authority on the subject of the movements of the heavenly bodies has held sway over the minds of men for so long a period as the fourteen centuries during which his opinions reigned supreme. The doctrines he laid down in his famous book, "The Almagest," prevailed throughout those ages. No substantial addition was made in all that time to the undoubted truths which this work contained. No important correction was made of the serious errors with which Ptolemy's theories were contaminated. The authority of Ptolemy as to all things in the heavens, and as to a good many things on the earth (for the same illustrious man was also a diligent geographer), was invariably final.

Though every child may now know more of the actual truths of the celestial motions than ever Ptolemy knew, yet the fact that his work exercised such an astonishing effect on the human intellect for some sixty generations, shows that it must have been an extraordinary production. We must look into the career of this wonderful man to discover wherein lay the secret of that marvellous success which made him the unchallenged instructor of the human race for such a protracted period.

Unfortunately, we know very little as to the personal history of Ptolemy. He was a native of Egypt, and though it has been sometimes conjectured that he belonged to the royal families of the same name, yet there is nothing to support such a belief. The name, Ptolemy, ap-

PTOLEMY

pears to have been a common one in Egypt in those days. The time at which he lived is fixed by the fact that his first recorded observation was made in 127 AD, and his last in 151 AD. When we add that he seems to have lived in or near Alexandria, or to use his own words, "on the parallel of Alexandria," we have said everything that can be said so far as his individuality is concerned.

Ptolemy is, without doubt, the greatest figure in ancient astronomy. He gathered up the wisdom of the philosophers who had preceded him. He incorporated this with the results of his own observations, and illumined it with his theories. His speculations, even when they were, as we now know, quite erroneous, had such an astonishing verisimilitude to the actual facts of nature that they commanded universal assent. Even in these modern days we not unfrequently find lovers of paradox who maintain that Ptolemy's doctrines not only seem true, but actually are true.

In the absence of any accurate knowledge of the science of mechanics, philosophers in early times were forced to fall back on certain principles of more or less validity, which they derived from their imagination as to what the natural fitness of things ought to be. There was no geometrical figure so simple and so symmetrical as a circle, and as it was apparent that the heavenly bodies pursued tracks which were not straight lines, the conclusion obviously followed that their movements ought to be circular. There was no argument in favour of this notion, other than the merely imaginary reflection that circular movement, and circular movement alone, was "perfect," whatever "perfect" may have meant. It was further believed to be impossible that the heavenly bodies could have any other movements save those which were perfect. Assuming this, it followed, in Ptolemy's opinion, and in that of those who came after him for fourteen centuries, that all the tracks of the heavenly bodies were in some way or other to be reduced to circles.

Ptolemy succeeded in devising a scheme by which the apparent changes that take place in the heavens could, so far as he knew them, be explained by certain combinations of circular movement. This seemed to reconcile so completely the scheme of things celestial with the geometrical instincts which pointed to the circle as the type of perfect movement, that we can hardly wonder Ptolemy's theory met with the astonishing success that attended it. We shall, therefore, set forth with sufficient detail the various steps of this famous doctrine.

Ptolemy commences with laying down the undoubted truth that the shape of the earth is globular. The proofs which he gives of this fundamental fact are quite satisfactory; they are indeed the same proofs as we give today. There is, first of all, the well-known circumstance of which our books on geography remind us, that when an object is viewed at a distance across the sea, the lower part of the object appears cut off by the interposing curved mass of water.

The sagacity of Ptolemy enabled him to adduce another argument, which, though not quite so obvious as that just mentioned, demonstrates the curvature of the earth in a very impressive manner to anyone who will take the trouble to understand it. Ptolemy mentions that travellers who went to the south reported, that, as they did so, the appearance of the heavens at night underwent a gradual change. Stars that they were familiar with in the northern skies gradually sank lower in the heavens. The constellation of the Great Bear, which in our skies never sets during its revolution round the pole, did set and rise when a sufficient southern latitude had been attained. On the other hand, constellations new to the inhabitants of northern climes were seen to rise above the southern horizon. These circumstances would be quite incompatible with the supposition that the earth was a flat surface. Had this been so, a little reflection will show that no such changes in the apparent movements of the stars would be the consequence of a voyage to the south. Ptolemy set forth with much insight the significance of this reasoning, and even now, with the resources of modern discoveries to help us, we can hardly improve upon his arguments.

Ptolemy, like a true philosopher disclosing a new truth to the world, illustrated and enforced his subject by a variety of happy demonstrations. I must add one of them, not only on account of its striking nature, but also because it exemplifies Ptolemy's acuteness. If the earth were flat, said this ingenious reasoner, sunset must necessarily take place at the same instant, no matter in what country the observer may happen to be placed. Ptolemy, however, proved that the time of sunset did vary greatly as the observer's longitude was altered. To us, of course, this is quite obvious; everybody knows that the hour of sunset may have been reached in Great Britain while it is still noon on the western coast of America. Ptolemy had, however, few of those sources of knowledge which are now accessible. How was he to show that the sun actually did set earlier at Alexandria than it would in a city which lay a hundred miles to the west? There was no telegraph wire by which astronomers at the two Places could communicate. There was no chronometer or watch which could be transported from place to place; there was not any other reliable contrivance for the keeping of time. Ptolemy's ingenuity, however, pointed out a thoroughly satisfactory method by which the times of sunset at two places could be compared. He was acquainted with the fact, which must indeed have been known from the very earliest times, that the illumination of the moon is derived entirely from the sun. He knew that an eclipse of the moon was due to the interposition of the earth which cuts off the light of the sun. It was, therefore, plain that an eclipse of the moon must be a phenomenon which would begin at the same instant from whatever part of the earth the moon could be seen at the time. Ptolemy, therefore, brought together from various quarters the local times at which different observers had recorded the beginning of a lunar eclipse. He found that the observers to the west made the time earlier and earlier the further away their stations were from Alexandria. On the other hand, the eastern observers set down the hour as later than that at which the phenomenon appeared at Alexandria. As these observers all recorded something which indeed appeared to them simultaneously, the only interpretation was, that the more easterly a place the later its time. Suppose there were a number of observers along a parallel of latitude, and each noted the hour of sunset to be six o'clock, then, since the eastern times are earlier than western times, 6 p.m. at one station A will correspond to 5 p.m. at a station B sufficiently to the west. If, therefore, it is sunset to the observer at A, the hour of sunset will not yet be reached for the observer at B. This proves conclusively that the time of sunset is not the same all over the earth. We have, however, already seen that the apparent time of sunset would be the same from all stations if the earth were flat. When Ptolemy, therefore, demonstrated that the time of sunset was not the same at various places, he showed conclusively that the earth was not flat.

As the same arguments applied to all parts of the earth where Ptolemy had either been himself, or from which he could gain the necessary information, it followed that the earth, instead of being the flat plain, girdled with an illimitable ocean, as was generally supposed, must be in reality globular. This led at once to a startling consequence. It was obvious that there could be no supports of any kind by which this globe was sustained; it therefore followed that the mighty object must be simply poised in space. This is indeed an astonishing doctrine to anyone who relies on what merely seems the evidence of the senses, without giving to that evidence its due intellectual interpretation. According to our ordinary experience, the very idea of an object poised without support in space, appears preposterous. Would it not fall? we are immediately asked. Yes, doubtless it could not remain poised in any way in which we try the experiment. We must, however, observe that there are no such ideas as upwards or downwards in relation to open space. To say that a body falls downwards, merely means that it tries to fall as nearly as possible towards the centre of the earth. There is no one direction along which a body will tend to move in space, in preference to any other. This may be illustrated by the fact that a stone let fall at New Zealand will, in its approach towards the earth's centre, be actually moving upwards as far as any locality in our hemisphere is concerned. Why, then, argued Ptolemy, may not the earth remain poised in space, for as all directions are equally upward or equally downward, there seems no reason why the earth should require any support? By this reasoning he arrives at the fundamental conclusion that the earth is a globular body freely lying in space, and surrounded above, below, and on all sides by the glittering stars of heaven.

The perception of this sublime truth marks a notable epoch in the history of the gradual development of the human intellect. No doubt, other philosophers, in groping after knowledge, may have set forth certain assertions that are more or less equivalent to this fundamental truth. It is to Ptolemy we must give credit, however, not only for announcing this doctrine, but for demonstrating it by clear and logical argument. We cannot easily project our minds back to the conception of an intellectual state in which this truth was unfamiliar. It may, however, be well imagined that, to one who thought the earth was a flat plain of indefinite extent, it would be nothing less than an intellectual convulsion for him to be forced to believe that he stood upon a spherical earth, forming merely a particle relatively to the immense sphere of the heavens.

What Ptolemy saw in the movements of the stars led him to the conclusion that they were bright points attached to the inside of a tremendous globe. The movements of this globe which carried the stars were only compatible with the supposition that the earth occupied its centre. The imperceptible effect produced by a change in the locality of the observer on the apparent brightness of the stars made it plain that the dimensions of the terrestrial globe must be quite insignificant in comparison with those of the celestial sphere. The earth might, in fact, be regarded as a grain of sand while the stars lay upon a globe many yards in diameter.

So tremendous was the revolution in human knowledge implied by this discovery, that we can well imagine how Ptolemy, dazzled as it were by the fame which had so justly accrued to him, failed to make one further step. Had he made that step, it would have emancipated the human intellect from the bondage of fourteen centuries of servitude to a wholly monstrous notion of this earth's importance in the scheme of the heavens. The obvious fact that the sun, the moon, and the stars rose day by day, moved across the sky in a glorious never-ending procession, and duly set when their appointed courses had been run, demanded some explanation. The circumstance that the fixed stars preserved their mutual distances from year to year, and from age to age, appeared to Ptolemy to prove that the sphere which contained those stars, and on whose surface they were believed by him to be fixed, revolved completely around the earth once every day. He would thus account for all the phenomena of rising and setting consistently with the supposition that our globe was stationary. Probably this supposition must have appeared monstrous, even to Ptolemy. He knew that the earth was a gigantic object, but, large as it may have been, he knew that it was only a particle in comparison with the celestial sphere, yet he apparently believed, and certainly succeeded in persuading other men to believe, that the celestial sphere did actually perform these movements.

Ptolemy was an excellent geometer. He knew that the rising and the setting of the sun, the moon, and the myriad stars, could have been accounted for in a different way. If the earth turned round uniformly once a day while poised at the centre of the sphere of the heavens, all the phenomena of rising and setting could be completely explained. This is, indeed, obvious after a moment's reflection. Consider yourself to be standing on the earth at the centre of the heavens. There are stars over your head, and half the contents of the heavens are visible, while the other half are below your horizon. As the earth turns round, the stars over your head will change, and unless it should happen that you have taken up your position at either of the poles, new stars will pass into your view, and others will disappear, for at no time can you have more than half of the whole sphere visible. The observer on the earth would, therefore, say that some stars were rising, and that some stars were setting. We have, therefore, two totally distinct methods, each of which would completely explain all the observed facts of the diurnal movement. One of these suppositions requires that the celestial sphere, bearing with it the stars and other celestial bodies, turns uniformly around an invisible axis, while the earth remains stationary at the centre. The other supposition would be, that it is the stupendous celestial sphere which remains stationary, while the earth at the centre rotates about the same axis as the celestial sphere did before, but in an opposite direction, and with a uniform velocity which would enable it to complete one turn in twenty-four hours. Ptolemy was mathematician enough to know that either of these suppositions would suffice for the explanation of the observed facts. Indeed, the phenomena of the movements of the stars, so far as he could observe them, could not be called upon to pronounce which of these views was true, and which was false.

Ptolemy had, therefore, to resort for guidance to indirect lines of reasoning. One of these suppositions must be true, and yet it appeared that the adoption of either was accompanied by a great difficulty. It is one of his chief merits to have demonstrated that the celestial sphere was so stupendous that the earth itself was absolutely insignificant in comparison therewith. If, then, this stupendous sphere rotated once in twenty-four hours, the speed with which the movement of some of the stars must be executed would be so portentous as to seem well-nigh impossible. It would, therefore, seem much simpler on this ground to adopt the other alternative, and to suppose the diurnal movements were due to the rotation of the earth. Here Ptolemy saw, or at all events fancied he saw, objections of the weightiest description. The evidence of the senses appeared directly to controvert the supposition that this earth is anything but stationary. Ptolemy might, perhaps, have dismissed this objection on the ground that the testimony of the senses on such a matter should be entirely subordinated to the interpretation which our intelligence would place upon the facts to which the senses deposed. Another objection, however, appeared to him to possess the gravest moment. It was argued that if the earth were rotating, there is nothing to make the air participate in this motion, mankind would therefore be swept from the earth by the furious blasts which would arise from the movement of the earth through an atmosphere at rest. Even if we could imagine that the air were carried round with the earth, the same would not apply, so thought Ptolemy, to any object suspended in the air. So long as a bird was perched on a tree, he might very well be carried onward by the moving earth, but the moment he took wing, the ground would slip from under him at a frightful pace, so that when he dropped down again he would find himself at a distance perhaps ten times as great as that which a carrier-pigeon or a swallow could have traversed in the same time. Some vague delusion of this description seems even still to crop up occasionally. I remember hearing of a proposition for balloon travelling of a very remarkable kind. The voyager who wanted to reach any other place in the same latitude was simply to ascend in a balloon, and wait there till the rotation of the earth conveyed the locality which happened to be his destination directly beneath him, whereupon he was to let out the gas and drop down! Ptolemy knew quite enough natural philosophy to be aware that such a proposal for locomotion would be an utter absurdity; he knew that there was no such relative shift between the air and the earth as this motion would imply. It appeared to him to be necessary that the air should lag behind, if the earth had been animated by a movement of rotation. In this he was, as we know, entirely wrong. There were, however, in his days no accurate notions on the subject of the laws of motion.

Assiduous as Ptolemy may have been in the study of the heavenly bodies, it seems evident that he cannot have devoted much thought to the phenomena of motion of terrestrial objects. Simple, indeed, are the experiments which might have convinced a philosopher much less acute than Ptolemy, that, if the earth did revolve, the air must necessarily accompany it. If a rider galloping on horseback tosses a ball into the air, it drops again into his hand, just as it would have done had he been remaining at rest during the ball's flight; the ball in fact participates in the horizontal motion, so that though it really describes a curve as any passer-by would observe, yet it appears to the rider himself merely to move up and down in a straight line. This fact, and many others similar to it, demonstrate clearly that if the earth were endowed with a movement of rotation, the atmosphere surrounding it must participate in that movement. Ptolemy did not know this, and consequently he came to the conclusion that the earth did not rotate, and that, therefore, notwithstanding the tremendous improbability of so mighty an object as the celestial sphere spinning round once in every twenty-four hours, there was no course open except to believe that this very improbable thing did really happen. Thus it came to pass that Ptolemy adopted as the cardinal doctrine of his system a stationary earth poised at the centre of the celestial sphere, which stretched around on all sides at a distance so vast that the diameter of the earth was an inappreciable point in comparison therewith.

Ptolemy having thus deliberately rejected the doctrine of the earth's rotation, had to make certain other entirely erroneous suppositions. It was easily seen that each star required exactly the same period for the performance of a complete revolution of the heavens. Ptolemy knew that the stars were at enormous distances from the earth, though no doubt his notions on this point came very far short of what we know to be the reality. If the stars had been at very varied distances, then it would be so wildly improbable that they should all accomplish their revolutions in the same time, that Ptolemy came to the conclusion that they must be all at the same distance, that is, that they must be all on the surface of a sphere. This view, however erroneous, was corroborated by the obvious fact that the stars in the constellations preserved their relative places unaltered for centuries. Thus it was that Ptolemy came to the conclusion that they were all fixed on one spherical surface, though we are not informed as to the material of this marvellous setting which sustained the stars like jewels.

Nor should we hastily pronounce this doctrine to be absurd. The stars do appear to lie on the surface of a sphere, of which the observer is at the centre; not only is this the aspect which the skies present to the untechnical observer, but it is the aspect in which the skies are presented to the most experienced astronomer of modern days. No doubt he knows well that the stars are at the most varied distances from him; he knows that certain stars are ten times, or a hundred times, or a thousand times, as far as other stars. Nevertheless, to his eye the stars appear on the surface of the sphere, it is on that surface that his measurements of the relative places of the stars are made; indeed, it may be said that almost all the accurate observations in the observatory relate to the places of the stars, not as they really are, but as they appear to be projected on that celestial sphere whose conception we owe to the genius of Ptolemy.

This great philosopher shows very ingeniously that the earth must be at the centre of the sphere. He proves that, unless this were the case, each star would not appear to move with the absolute uniformity which does, as a matter of fact, characterise it. In all these reasonings we cannot but have the most profound admiration for the genius of Ptolemy, even though he had made an error so enormous in the fundamental point of the stability of the earth. Another error of a somewhat similar kind seemed to Ptolemy to be demonstrated. He had shown that the earth was an isolated object in space, and being such was, of course, capable of movement. It could either be turned round, or it could be moved from one place to another. We know that Ptolemy deliberately adopted the view that the earth did not turn round; he had then to investigate the other question, as to whether the earth was animated by any movement of translation. He came to the conclusion that to attribute any motion to the earth would be incompatible with the truths at which he had already arrived. The earth, argued Ptolemy, lies at the centre of the celestial sphere. If the earth were to be endowed with movement, it would not lie always at this point, it must, therefore, shift to some other part of the sphere. The movements of the stars, however, preclude the possibility of this; and, therefore, the earth must be as devoid of any movement of translation as it is devoid of rotation. Thus it was that Ptolemy convinced himself that the stability of the earth, as it appeared to the ordinary senses, had a rational philosophical foundation.

Not unfrequently it is the lot of the philosophers to contend against the doctrines of the vulgar, but when it happens, as in the case of Ptolemy's researches, that the doctrines of the vulgar are corroborated by philosophical investigation which bear the stamp of the highest authority, it is not to be wondered at that such doctrines should be deemed well-nigh impregnable. In this way we may, perhaps, account for the remarkable fact that the theories of Ptolemy held unchallenged sway over the human intellect for the vast period already mentioned.

Up to the present we have been speaking only of those primary motions of the heavens, by which the whole sphere appeared to revolve once every twenty-four hours. We have now to discuss the remarkable theories by which Ptolemy endeavoured to account for the monthly movement of the moon, for the annual movement of the sun, and for the periodic movements of the planets which had gained for them the titles of the wandering stars.

Possessed with the idea that these movements must be circular, or must be capable, directly or indirectly, of being explained by circular movements, it seemed obvious to Ptolemy, as indeed it had done to previous astronomers, that the track of the moon through the stars was a circle of which the earth is the centre. A similar movement with a yearly period must also be attributed to the sun, for the changes in the positions of the constellations in accordance with the progress of the seasons, placed it beyond doubt that the sun made a circuit of the celestial sphere, even though the bright light of the sun prevented the stars in its vicinity, from being seen in daylight. Thus the movements both of the sun and the moon, as well as the diurnal rotation of the celestial sphere, seemed to justify the notion that all celestial movements must be "perfect," that is to say, described uniformly in those circles which were the only perfect curves.

The simplest observations, however, show that the movements of the planets cannot be explained in this simple fashion. Here the geometrical genius of Ptolemy shone forth, and he devised a scheme by which the apparent wanderings of the planets could be accounted for without the introduction of aught save "perfect" movements.

To understand his reasoning, let us first set forth clearly those facts of observation which require to be explained. I shall take, in particular, two planets, Venus and Mars, as these illustrate, in the most striking manner, the peculiarities of the inner and the outer planets respectively. The simplest observations would show that Venus did not move round the heavens in the same fashion as the sun or the moon. Look at the evening star when brightest, as it appears in the west after sunset. Instead of moving towards the east among the stars, like the sun or the moon, we find, week after week, that Venus is drawing in towards the sun, until it is lost in the sunbeams. Then the planet emerges on the other side, not to be seen as an evening star, but as a morning star. In fact, it was plain that in some ways Venus accompanied the sun in its annual movement. Now it is found advancing in front of the sun to a certain limited distance, and now it is lagging to an equal extent behind the sun.

These movements were wholly incompatible with the supposition that the journeys of Venus were described by a single motion of the kind regarded as perfect. It was obvious that the movement was connected in some strange manner with the revolution of the sun, and here was the ingenious method by which Ptolemy sought to render account of it. Imagine a fixed arm to extend from the earth to the sun, as shown in the accompanying figure (Fig. 1), then this arm will move round uniformly, in consequence of the sun's movement. At a point P on this arm let a small circle be described. Venus is supposed to revolve uniformly in this small circle, while the circle itself is carried round continuously by the movement of the sun. In this way it was possible to account for the chief peculiarities in the movement of Venus. It will be seen that, in consequence of the revolution around P, the spectator on the earth will sometimes see Venus on one side of the sun, and sometimes on the other side, so that the planet always remains in the sun's vicinity. By properly proportioning the movements, this little contrivance simulated the transitions from the morning star to the evening star. Thus the changes of Venus could be accounted for by a Combination of the "perfect" movement of P in the circle which it described uniformly round the earth, combined with the "perfect" motion of Venus in the circle which it described uniformly around the moving centre.

In a precisely similar manner Ptolemy rendered an explanation of the fitful apparitions of Mercury. Now just on one side of the sun, and now just on the other, this rarely-seen planet moved like Venus on a circle whereof the centre was also carried by the line joining the sun and the earth. The circle, however, in which Mercury actually revolved had to be smaller than that of Venus, in order to account for the fact that Mercury lies always much closer to the sun than the better-known planet.

The explanation of the movement of an outer planet like Mars could also be deduced from the joint effect of two perfect motions. The changes through which Mars goes are, however, so different from the movements of Venus that quite a different disposition of the circles is necessary. For consider the facts which characterise the movements of an outer planet such as Mars. In the first place, Mars accomplishes an entire circuit of the heaven. In this respect, no doubt, it may be said to resemble the sun or the moon. A little attention will, however, show that there are extraordinary irregularities in the movement of the planet. Generally speaking, it speeds its way from west to east among

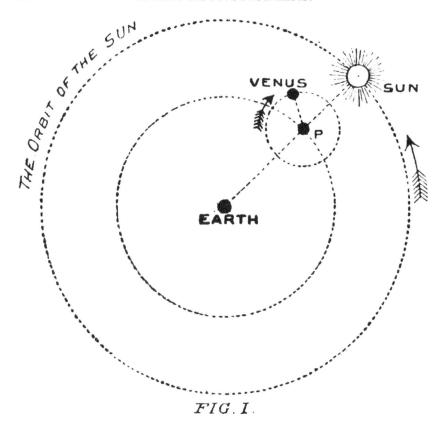

FIG. I.

the stars, but sometimes the attentive observer will note that the speed with which the planet advances is slackening, and then it will seem to become stationary. Some days later the direction of the planet's movement will be reversed, and it will be found moving from the east towards the west. At first it proceeds slowly and then quickens its pace, until a certain speed is attained, which afterwards declines until a second stationary position is reached. After a due pause the original motion from west to east is resumed, and is continued until a similar cycle of changes again commences. Such movements as these were obviously quite at variance with any perfect movement in a single circle round the earth. Here, again, the geometrical sagacity of Ptolemy provided him with the means of representing the apparent movements of Mars, and, at the same time, restricting the explanation to those perfect movements which he deemed so essential. In Fig. 2 we exhibit Ptolemy's theory as to the movement of Mars. We have, as before, the

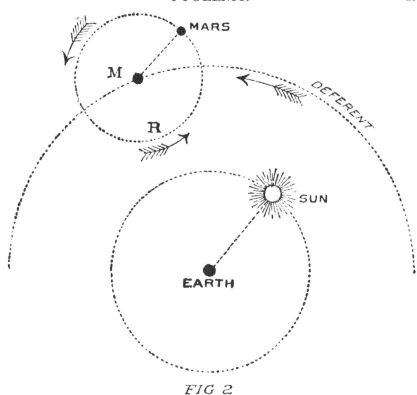

FIG 2

earth at the centre, and the sun describing its circular orbit around that centre. The path of Mars is to be taken as exterior to that of the sun. We are to suppose that at a point marked M there is a fictitious planet, which revolves around the earth uniformly, in a circle called the *deferent*. This point M, which is thus animated by a perfect movement, is the centre of a circle which is carried onwards with M, and around the circumference of which Mars revolves uniformly. It is easy to show that the combined effect of these two perfect movements is to produce exactly that displacement of Mars in the heavens which observation discloses. In the position represented in the figure, Mars is obviously pursuing a course which will appear to the observer as a movement from west to east. When, however, the planet gets round to such a position as R, it is then moving from east to west in consequence of its revolution in the moving circle, as indicated by the arrow-head. On the other hand, the whole circle is carried forward in the opposite direction. If the latter movement be less rapid than the former, then we shall have the backward movement of Mars on the heavens which it was desired to explain. By a proper adjustment of the relative lengths of these arms the movements of the planet as actually observed could be completely accounted for.

The other outer planets with which Ptolemy was acquainted, namely, Jupiter and Saturn, had movements of the same general character as those of Mars. Ptolemy was equally successful in explaining the movements they performed by the supposition that each planet had perfect rotation in a circle of its own, which circle itself had perfect movement around the earth in the centre.

It is somewhat strange that Ptolemy did not advance one step further, as by so doing he would have given great simplicity to his system. He might, for instance, have represented the movements of Venus equally well by putting the centre of the moving circle at the sun itself, and correspondingly enlarging the circle in which Venus revolved. He might, too, have arranged that the several circles which the outer planets traversed should also have had their centres at the sun. The planetary system would then have consisted of an earth fixed at the centre, of a sun revolving uniformly around it, and of a system of planets each describing its own circle around a moving centre placed in the sun. Perhaps Ptolemy had not thought of this, or perhaps he may have seen arguments against it. This important step was, however, taken by Tycho. He considered that all the planets revolved around the sun in circles, and that the sun itself, bearing all these orbits, described a mighty circle around the earth. This point having been reached, only one more step would have been necessary to reach the glorious truths that revealed the structure of the solar system. That last step was taken by Copernicus.

COPERNICUS.

The quaint town of Thorn, on the Vistula, was more than two centuries old when Copernicus was born there on the 19th of February, 1473. The situation of this town on the frontier between Prussia and Poland, with the commodious waterway offered by the river, made it a place of considerable trade. A view of the town, as it was at the time of the birth of Copernicus, is here given. The walls, with their watchtowers, will be noted, and the strategic importance which the situation of Thorn gave to it in the fifteenth century still belongs thereto, so much so that the German Government recently constituted the town a fortress of the first class.

Copernicus, the astronomer, whose discoveries make him the great predecessor of Kepler and Newton, did not come from a noble family, as certain other early astronomers have done, for his father was a tradesman. Chroniclers are, however, careful to tell us that one of his uncles was a bishop. We are not acquainted with any of those details of his childhood or youth which are often of such interest in other cases where men have risen to exalted fame. It would appear that the young Nicolaus, for such was his Christian name, received his education at home until such time as he was deemed sufficiently advanced to be sent to the University at Cracow. The education that he there obtained must have been in those days of a very primitive description, but Copernicus seems to have availed himself of it to the utmost. He devoted himself more particularly to the study of medicine, with the view of adopting its practice as the profession of his life. The tendencies of the future astronomer were, however, revealed in the fact that he worked hard at mathematics, and, like one of his illustrious successors, Galileo, the practice of the art of painting had for him a very great interest, and in it he obtained some measure of success.

By the time he was twenty-seven years old, it would seem that Copernicus had given up the notion of becoming a medical practitioner, and had resolved to devote himself to science. He was engaged in teaching mathematics, and appears to have acquired some reputation. His growing fame attracted the notice of his uncle the bishop, at whose suggestion Copernicus took holy orders, and he was presently appointed to a canonry in the cathedral of Frauenburg, near the mouth of the Vistula.

THORN, FROM AN OLD PRINT.

To Frauenburg, accordingly, this man of varied gifts retired. Possessing somewhat of the ascetic spirit, he resolved to devote his life to work of the most serious description. He eschewed all ordinary society, restricting his intimacies to very grave and learned companions, and refusing to engage in conversation of any useless kind. It would seem as if his gifts for painting were condemned as frivolous; at all events, we do not learn that he continued to practise them. In addition to the discharge of his theological duties, his life was occupied partly in ministering medically to the wants of the poor, and partly with his researches in astronomy and mathematics. His equipment in the matter of instruments for the study of the heavens seems to have been of a very meagre description. He arranged apertures in the

COPERNICUS.

walls of his house at Allenstein, so that he could observe in some fashion the passage of the stars across the meridian. That he possessed
some talent for practical mechanics is proved by his construction of a
contrivance for raising water from a stream, for the use of the inhabitants of Frauenburg. Relics of this machine are still to be seen.

The intellectual slumber of the Middle Ages was destined to be
awakened by the revolutionary doctrines of Copernicus. It may be
noted, as an interesting circumstance, that the time at which he discovered the scheme of the solar system has coincided with a remarkable
epoch in the world's history. The great astronomer had just reached
manhood at the time when Columbus discovered the new world.

Before the publication of the researches of Copernicus, the orthodox scientific creed averred that the earth was stationary, and that the
apparent movements of the heavenly bodies were indeed real move-

ments. Ptolemy had laid down this doctrine 1,400 years before. In his theory this huge error was associated with so much important truth, and the whole presented such a coherent scheme for the explanation of the heavenly movements, that the Ptolemaic theory was not seriously questioned until the great work of Copernicus appeared. No doubt others, before Copernicus, had from time to time in some vague fashion surmised, with more or less plausibility, that the sun, and not the earth, was the centre about which the system really revolved. It is, however, one thing to state a scientific fact; it is quite another thing to be in possession of the train of reasoning, founded on observation or experiment, by which that fact may be established. Pythagoras, it appears, had indeed told his disciples that it was the sun, and not the earth, which was the centre of movement, but it does not seem at all certain that Pythagoras had any grounds which science could recognise for the belief which is attributed to him. So far as information is available to us, it would seem that Pythagoras associated his scheme of things celestial with a number of preposterous notions in natural philosophy. He may certainly have made a correct statement as to which was the most important body in the solar system, but he certainly did not provide any rational demonstration of the fact. Copernicus, by a strict train of reasoning, convinced those who would listen to him that the sun was the centre of the system. It is useful for us to consider the arguments which he urged, and by which he effected that intellectual revolution which is always connected with his name.

The first of the great discoveries which Copernicus made relates to the rotation of the earth on its axis. That general diurnal movement, by which the stars and all other celestial bodies appear to be carried completely round the heavens once every twenty-four hours, had been accounted for by Ptolemy on the supposition that the apparent movements were the real movements. As we have already seen, Ptolemy himself felt the extraordinary difficulty involved in the supposition that so stupendous a fabric as the celestial sphere should spin in the way supposed. Such movements required that many of the stars should travel with almost inconceivable velocity. Copernicus also saw that the daily rising and setting of the heavenly bodies could be accounted for either by the supposition that the celestial sphere moved round and that the earth remained at rest, or by the supposition that the celestial sphere was at rest while the earth turned round in the opposite direction. He weighed the arguments on both sides as Ptolemy had done, and, as the result of his deliberations, Copernicus came to an opposite conclusion from Ptolemy. To Copernicus it appeared that the difficulties attending the supposition that the celestial sphere revolved, were vastly greater than those which appeared so weighty to Ptolemy as to force him to deny the earth's rotation.

Copernicus shows clearly how the observed phenomena could be accounted for just as completely by a rotation of the earth as by a rotation of the heavens. He alludes to the fact that, to those on board a vessel which is moving through smooth water, the vessel itself appears to be at rest, while the objects on shore seem to be moving past. If, therefore, the earth were rotating uniformly, we dwellers upon the earth, oblivious of our own movement, would wrongly attribute to the stars the displacement which was actually the consequence of our own motion.

Copernicus saw the futility of the arguments by which Ptolemy had endeavoured to demonstrate that a revolution of the earth was impossible. It was plain to him that there was nothing whatever to warrant refusal to believe in the rotation of the earth. In his clear-sightedness on this matter we have specially to admire the sagacity of Copernicus as a natural philosopher. It had been urged that, if the earth moved round, its motion would not be imparted to the air, and that therefore the earth would be uninhabitable by the terrific winds which would be the result of our being carried through the air. Copernicus convinced himself that this deduction was preposterous. He proved that the air must accompany the earth, just as his coat remains round him, notwithstanding the fact that he is walking down the street. In this way he was able to show that all a priori objections to the earth's movements were absurd, and therefore he was able to compare together the plausibilities of the two rival schemes for explaining the diurnal movement.

Once the issue had been placed in this form, the result could not be long in doubt. Here is the question: Which is it more likely—that the earth, like a grain of sand at the centre of a mighty globe, should turn round once in twenty-four hours, or that the whole of that vast globe should complete a rotation in the opposite direction in the same time? Obviously, the former is far the more simple supposition. But the case is really much stronger than this. Ptolemy had supposed that all the stars were attached to the surface of a sphere. He had no ground whatever for this supposition, except that otherwise it would have been well-nigh impossible to have devised a scheme by which the rotation of the heavens around a fixed earth could have been arranged. Copernicus, however, with the just instinct of a philosopher, considered that the celestial sphere, however convenient from a geometrical point of view, as a means of representing apparent phenomena, could not actually have a material existence. In the first place, the existence of a material celestial sphere would require that all the myriad stars should be at exactly the same distances from the earth. Of course, no one will say that this or any other arbitrary disposition of the stars is actually impossible, but as there was no conceivable physical reason why the distances of all the stars from the earth should be identical, it seemed in the very highest degree improbable that the stars should be so placed.

Doubtless, also, Copernicus felt a considerable difficulty as to the nature of the materials from which Ptolemy's wonderful sphere was to be constructed. Nor could a philosopher of his penetration have failed to observe that, unless that sphere were infinitely large, there must have been space outside it, a consideration which would open up other difficult questions. Whether infinite or not, it was obvious that the celestial sphere must have a diameter at least many thousands of times as great as that of the earth. From these considerations Copernicus deduced the important fact that the stars and the other celestial bodies must all be vast objects. He was thus enabled to put the question in such a form that it could hardly receive any answer but the correct one. Which is it more rational to suppose, that the earth should turn round on its axis once in twenty-four hours, or that thousands of mighty stars should circle round the earth in the same time, many of them having to describe circles many thousands of times greater in circumference than the circuit of the earth at the equator? The obvious answer pressed upon Copernicus with so much force that he was compelled to reject Ptolemy's theory of the stationary earth, and to attribute the diurnal rotation of the heavens to the revolution of the earth on its axis.

Once this tremendous step had been taken, the great difficulties which beset the monstrous conception of the celestial sphere vanished,

FRAUENBURG. FROM AN OLD PRINT.

for the stars need no longer be regarded as situated at equal distances from the earth. Copernicus saw that they might lie at the most varied degrees of remoteness, some being hundreds or thousands of times farther away than others. The complicated structure of the celestial sphere as a material object disappeared altogether; it remained only as a geometrical conception, whereon we find it convenient to indicate the places of the stars. Once the Copernican doctrine had been fully set forth, it was impossible for anyone, who had both the inclination and the capacity to understand it, to withhold acceptance of its truth. The doctrine of a stationary earth had gone for ever.

Copernicus having established a theory of the celestial movements which deliberately set aside the stability of the earth, it seemed natural that he should inquire whether the doctrine of a moving earth might not remove the difficulties presented in other celestial phenomena. It had been universally admitted that the earth lay unsupported in space. Copernicus had further shown that it possessed a movement of rotation. Its want of stability being thus recognised, it seemed reasonable to suppose that the earth might also have some other kinds of movements as well. In this, Copernicus essayed to solve a problem far more difficult than that which had hitherto occupied his attention. It was a comparatively easy task to show how the diurnal rising and setting could be accounted for by the rotation of the earth. It was a much more difficult undertaking to demonstrate that the planetary movements, which Ptolemy had represented with so much success, could be completely explained by the supposition that each of those planets revolved uniformly round the sun, and that the earth was also a planet, accomplishing a complete circuit of the sun once in the course of a year.

It would be impossible in a sketch like the present to enter into any detail as to the geometrical propositions on which this beautiful investigation of Copernicus depended. We can only mention a few of the leading principles. It may be laid down in general that, if an observer is in movement, he will, if unconscious of the fact, attribute to the fixed objects around him a movement equal and opposite to that which he actually possesses. A passenger on a canal-boat sees the objects on the banks apparently moving backward with a speed equal to that by which he is himself advancing forwards. By an application of this prin-

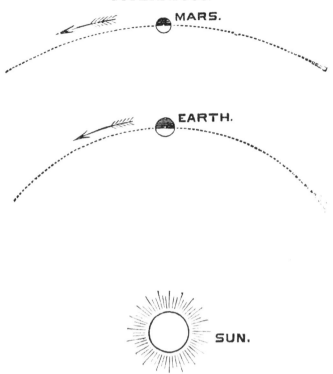

ciple, we can account for all the phenomena of the movements of the planets, which Ptolemy had so ingeniously represented by his circles. Let us take, for instance, the most characteristic feature in the irregularities of the outer planets. We have already remarked that Mars, though generally advancing from west to east among the stars, occasionally pauses, retraces his steps for awhile, again pauses, and then resumes his ordinary onward progress. Copernicus showed clearly how this effect was produced by the real motion of the earth, combined with the real motion of Mars. In the adjoining figure we represent a portion of the circular tracks in which the earth and Mars move in accordance with the Copernican doctrine. I show particularly the case where the earth comes directly between the planet and the sun, because it is on such occasions that the retrograde movement (for so this backward movement of Mars is termed) is at its highest. Mars is then advancing in the direction shown by the arrow-head, and the earth is also advancing in the same direction. We, on the earth, however, being unconscious of our own motion, attribute, by the principle I have already explained, an equal and opposite motion to Mars. The visible effect upon the planet is, that Mars has two movements, a real onward movement in one direction, and an apparent movement in the opposite direction. If it so happened that the earth was moving with the same speed as Mars, then the apparent movement would exactly neutralise the real movement, and Mars would seem to be at rest relatively to the surrounding stars. Under the actual circumstances represented, however, the earth is moving faster than Mars, and the consequence is, that the apparent movement of the planet backwards exceeds the real movement forwards, the net result being an apparent retrograde movement.

With consummate skill, Copernicus showed how the applications of the same principles could account for the characteristic movements of the planets. His reasoning in due time bore down all opposition. The supreme importance of the earth in the system vanished. It had now merely to take rank as one of the planets.

The same great astronomer now, for the first time, rendered something like a rational account of the changes of the seasons. Nor did certain of the more obscure astronomical phenomena escape his attention.

He delayed publishing his wonderful discoveries to the world until he was quite an old man. He had a well-founded apprehension of the storm of opposition which they would arouse. However, he yielded at last to the entreaties of his friends, and his book was sent to the press. But ere it made its appearance to the world, Copernicus was seized by mortal illness. A copy of the book was brought to him on May 23, 1543. We are told that he was able to see it and to touch it, but no more, and he died a few hours afterwards. He was buried in that Cathedral of Frauenburg, with which his life had been so closely associated.

TYCHO BRAHE.

The most picturesque figure in the history of astronomy is undoubtedly that of the famous old Danish astronomer whose name stands at the head of this chapter. Tycho Brahe was alike notable for his astronomical genius and for the extraordinary vehemence of a character which was by no means perfect. His romantic career as a philosopher, and his taste for splendour as a Danish noble, his ardent friendships and his furious quarrels, make him an ideal subject for a biographer, while the magnificent astronomical work which he accomplished, has given him imperishable fame.

The history of Tycho Brahe has been admirably told by Dr. Dreyer, the accomplished astronomer who now directs the observatory at Armagh, though himself a countryman of Tycho. Every student of the career of the great Dane must necessarily look on Dr. Dreyer's work as the chief authority on the subject. Tycho sprang from an illustrious stock. His family had flourished for centuries, both in Sweden and in Denmark, where his descendants are to be met with at the present day. The astronomer's father was a privy councillor, and having filled important positions in the Danish government, he was ultimately promoted to be governor of Helsingborg Castle, where he spent the last years of his life. His illustrious son Tycho was born in 1546, and was the second child and eldest boy in a family of ten.

It appears that Otto, the father of Tycho, had a brother named George, who was childless. George, however, desired to adopt a boy on whom he could lavish his affection and to whom he could bequeath his wealth. A somewhat singular arrangement was accordingly entered into by the brothers at the time when Otto was married. It was agreed that the first son who might be born to Otto should be forthwith handed over by the parents to George to be reared and adopted by him. In due time little Tycho appeared, and was immediately claimed by George in pursuance of the compact. But it was not unnatural that the parental instinct, which had been dormant when the agreement was made, should here interpose. Tycho's father and mother receded from the bargain, and refused to part with their son. George thought he was badly treated. However, he took no violent steps until a year later, when a brother was born to Tycho. The uncle then felt no scruple in asserting what he believed to be his rights by the simple process of stealing the first-born nephew, which the original bargain had promised him. After a little time it would seem that the parents acquiesced in the loss, and thus it was in Uncle George's home that the future astronomer passed his childhood.

When we read that Tycho was no more than thirteen years old at the time he entered the University of Copenhagen, it might be at first supposed that even in his boyish years he must have exhibited some of those remarkable talents with which he was afterwards to astonish the world. Such an inference should not, however, be drawn. The fact is that in those days it was customary for students to enter the universities at a much earlier age than is now the case. Not, indeed, that the boys of thirteen knew more then than the boys of thirteen know now. But the education imparted in the universities at that time was of a much more rudimentary kind than that which we understand by university education at present. In illustration of this Dr. Dreyer tells us how, in the University of Wittenberg, one of the professors, in his opening address, was accustomed to point out that even the processes of multiplication and division in arithmetic might be learned by any student who possessed the necessary diligence.

It was the wish and the intention of his uncle that Tycho's education should be specially directed to those branches of rhetoric and philosophy which were then supposed to be a necessary preparation for the career of a statesman. Tycho, however, speedily made it plain to his teachers that though he was an ardent student, yet the things which interested him were the movements of the heavenly bodies and not the subtleties of metaphysics.

On the 21st October, 1560, an eclipse of the sun occurred, which was partially visible at Copenhagen. Tycho, boy though he was, took

TYCHO BRAHE.

the utmost interest in this event. His ardour and astonishment in connection with the circumstance were chiefly excited by the fact that the time of the occurrence of the phenomenon could be predicted with so much accuracy. Urged by his desire to understand the matter thoroughly, Tycho sought to procure some book which might explain what he so greatly wanted to know. In those days books of any kind were but few and scarce, and scientific books were especially unattainable. It so happened, however, that a Latin version of Ptolemy's astronomical works had appeared a few years before the eclipse took place, and Tycho managed to buy a copy of this book, which was then the chief authority on celestial matters. Young as the boy astronomer was,

he studied hard, although perhaps not always successfully, to understand Ptolemy, and to this day his copy of the great work, copiously
annotated and marked by the schoolboy hand, is preserved as one of
the chief treasures in the library of the University at Prague.

After Tycho had studied for about three years at the University of
Copenhagen, his uncle thought it would be better to send him, as was
usual in those days, to complete his education by a course of study in
some foreign university. The uncle cherished the hope that in this way
the attention of the young astronomer might be withdrawn from the
study of the stars and directed in what appeared to him a more useful
way. Indeed, to the wise heads of those days, the pursuit of natural science seemed so much waste of good time which might otherwise be
devoted to logic or rhetoric or some other branch of study more in
vogue at that time. To assist in this attempt to wean Tycho from his
scientific tastes, his uncle chose as a tutor to accompany him an intelli-
gent and upright young man named Vedel, who was four years senior
to his pupil, and accordingly, in 1562, we find the pair taking up their
abode at the University of Leipzig.

The tutor, however, soon found that he had undertaken a most
hopeless task. He could not succeed in imbuing Tycho with the slightest taste for the study of the law or the other branches of knowledge
which were then thought so desirable. The stars, and nothing but the
stars, engrossed the attention of his pupil. We are told that all the
money he could obtain was spent secretly in buying astronomical
books and instruments. He learned the name of the stars from a little
globe, which he kept hidden from Vedel, and only ventured to use during the latter's absence. No little friction was at first caused by all this,
but in after years a fast and enduring friendship grew up between Tycho and his tutor, each of whom learned to respect and to love the
other.

Before Tycho was seventeen he had commenced the difficult task of
calculating the movements of the planets and the places which they occupied on the sky from time to time. He was not a little surprised to
find that the actual positions of the planets differed very widely from
those which were assigned to them by calculations from the best existing works of astronomers. With the insight of genius he saw that the
only true method of investigating the movements of the heavenly bod-

ies would be to carry on a protracted series of measurements of their places. This, which now seems to us so obvious, was then entirely new doctrine. Tycho at once commenced regular observations in such fashion as he could. His first instrument was, indeed, a very primitive one, consisting of a simple pair of compasses, which he used in this way. He placed his eye at the hinge, and then opened the legs of the compass so that one leg pointed to one star and the other leg to the other star. The compass was then brought down to a divided circle, by which means the number of degrees in the apparent angular distance of the two stars was determined.

His next advance in instrumental equipment was to provide himself with the contrivance known as the "cross-staff," which he used to observe the stars whenever opportunity offered. It must, of course, be remembered that in those days there were no telescopes. In the absence of optical aid, such as lenses afford the modern observers, astronomers had to rely on mechanical appliances alone to measure the places of the stars. Of such appliances, perhaps the most ingenious was one known before Tycho's time, which we have represented in the adjoining figure.

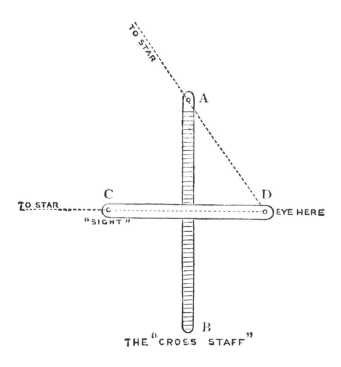

THE "CROSS STAFF"

Let us suppose that it be desired to measure the angle between two stars, then if the angle be not too large it can be determined in the following manner. Let the rod AB be divided into inches and parts of an inch, and let another rod, CD, slide up and down along AB in such a way that the two always remain perpendicular to each other. "Sights," like those on a rifle, are placed at A and C, and there is a pin at D. It will easily be seen that, by sliding the movable bar along the fixed one, it must always be possible when the stars are not too far apart to bring the sights into such positions that one star can be seen along DC and the other along DA. This having been accomplished, the length from A to the cross-bar is read off on the scale, and then, by means of a table previously prepared, the value of the required angular distance is obtained. If the angle between the two stars were greater than it would be possible to measure in the way already described, then there was a provision by which the pin at D might be moved along CD into some other position, so as to bring the angular distance of the stars within the range of the instrument.

No doubt the cross-staff is a very primitive contrivance, but when handled by one so skilful as Tycho it afforded results of considerable accuracy. I would recommend any reader who may have a taste for such pursuits to construct a cross-staff for himself, and see what measurements he can accomplish with its aid.

To employ this little instrument Tycho had to evade the vigilance of his conscientious tutor, who felt it his duty to interdict all such occupations as being a frivolous waste of time. It was when Vedel was asleep

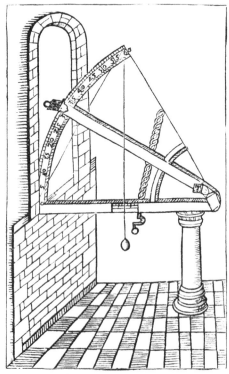

TYCHO'S "NEW STAR" SEXTANT
(The arms, of walnut wood, are about 5.5 ft. long.)

that Tycho managed to escape with his cross staff and measure the places of the heavenly bodies. Even at this early age Tycho used to conduct his observations on those thoroughly sound principles which lie at the foundation of all accurate modern astronomy. Recognising the inevitable errors of workmanship in his little instrument, he ascertained their amount and allowed for their influence on the results which he deduced. This principle, employed by the boy with his cross-staff in 1564, is employed at the present day by the Astronomer Royal at Greenwich with the most superb instruments that the skill of modern opticians has been able to construct.

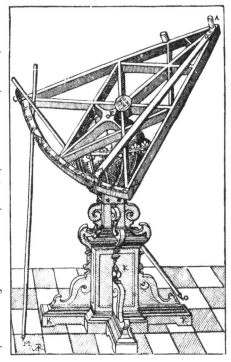

TYCHO'S TRIGONIC SEXTANT
(The arms, AB and AC, are about 5.5 ft. long.)

After the death of his uncle, when Tycho was nineteen years of age, it appears that the young philosopher was no longer interfered with in so far as the line which his studies were to take was concerned. Always of a somewhat restless temperament, we now find that he shifted his abode to the University of Rostock, where he speedily made himself notable in connection with an eclipse of the moon on 28th October, 1566. Like every other astronomer of those days, Tycho had always associated astronomy with astrology. He considered that the phenomena of the heavenly bodies always had some significance in connection with human affairs. Tycho was also a poet, and in the united capacity of poet, astrologer, and astronomer, he posted up some verses in the college at Rostock announcing that the lunar eclipse was a prognostication of the death of the great Turkish Sultan, whose mighty deeds at that time filled men's minds. Presently news did arrive of the death of the Sultan, and Tycho was accordingly triumphant; but a little later it

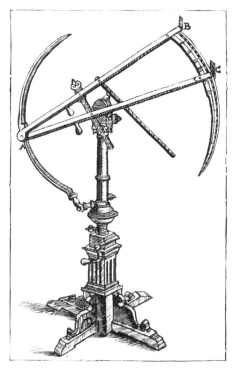

TYCHO'S ASTRONOMIC SEXTANT
(Made of steel; the arms, A B, A C, measure 4ft.)

appeared that the decease had taken place BEFORE the eclipse, a circumstance which caused many a laugh at Tycho's expense.

Tycho being of a somewhat turbulent disposition, it appears that, while at the University of Rostock, he had a serious quarrel with another Danish nobleman. We are not told for certain what was the cause of the dispute. It does not, however, seem to have had any more romantic origin than a difference of opinion as to which of them knew the more mathematics. They fought, as perhaps it was becoming for two astronomers to fight, under the canopy of heaven in utter darkness at the dead of night, and the duel was honourably terminated when a slice was taken off Tycho's nose by the insinuating sword of his antagonist. For the repair of this injury the ingenuity of the great instrument-maker was here again useful, and he made a substitute for his nose "with a composition of gold and silver." The imitation was so good that it is declared to have been quite equal to the original. Dr. Lodge, however, pointedly observes that it does not appear whether this remark was made by a friend or an enemy.

The next few years Tycho spent in various places ardently pursuing somewhat varied branches of scientific study. At one time we hear of him assisting an astronomical alderman, in the ancient city of Augsburg, to erect a tremendous wooden machine—a quadrant of 19-feet radius—to be used in observing the heavens. At another time we learn that the King of Denmark had recognised the talents of his illustrious subject, and promised to confer on him a pleasant sinecure in the shape of a canonry, which would assist him with the means for indulging his scientific pursuits. Again we are told that Tycho is pursuing experiments in chemistry with the greatest energy, nor is this so incompatible as might at first be thought with his devotion to astronomy. In those early days of knowledge the different sciences seemed bound together by mysterious bonds. Alchemists and astrologers taught that the several planets were correlated in some mysterious manner with the several metals. It was, therefore hardly surprising that Tycho should have included a study of the properties of the metals in the programme of his astronomical work.

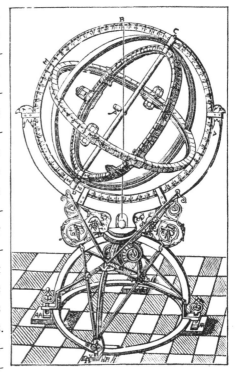

TYCHO'S EQUATORIAL ARMILLARY
(The meridian circle, E B C A D, made of solid steel, is nearly 6 ft. in diameter.)

An event, however, occurred in 1572 which stimulated Tycho's astronomical labours, and started him on his life's work. On the 11th of November in that year, he was returning home to supper after a day's work in his laboratory, when he happened to lift his face to the sky, and there he beheld a brilliant new star. It was in the constellation of Cassiopeia, and occupied a position in which there had certainly been no bright star visible when his attention had last been directed to that part of the heavens. Such a phenomenon was so startling that he found it hard to trust the evidence of his senses. He thought he must be the subject of some hallucination. He therefore called to the servants who were accompanying him, and asked them whether they, too, could see a brilliant object in the direction in which he pointed. They certainly could, and thus he became convinced that this marvellous object was no mere creation of the fancy, but a veritable celestial body—a new star of surpassing splendour which had suddenly burst forth. In these days

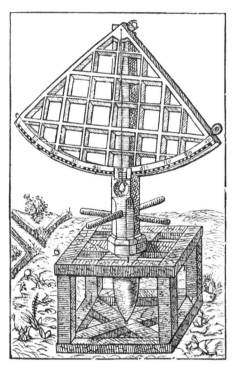

THE GREAT AUGSBURG QUADRANT.
(Built of heart of oak' the radii about 19 ft.)

of careful scrutiny of the heavens, we are accustomed to the occasional outbreak of new stars. It is not, however, believed that any new star which has ever appeared has displayed the same phenomenal brilliance as was exhibited by the star of 1572.

This object has a value in astronomy far greater than it might at first appear. It is true, in one sense, that Tycho discovered the new star, but it is equally true, in a different sense, that it was the new star which discovered Tycho. Had it not been for this opportune apparition, it is quite possible that Tycho might have found a career in some direction less beneficial to science than that which he ultimately pursued.

When he reached his home on this memorable evening, Tycho immediately applied his great quadrant to the measurement of the place of the new star. His observations were specially directed to the determination of the distance of the object. He rightly conjectured that if it were very much nearer to us than the stars in its vicinity, the distance of the brilliant body might be determined in a short time by the apparent changes in its distance from the surrounding points. It was speedily demonstrated that the new star could not be as near as the moon, by the simple fact that its apparent place, as compared with the stars in its neighbourhood, was not appreciably altered when it was observed below the pole, and again above the pole at an interval of twelve hours. Such observations were possible, inasmuch as the star was bright enough to be seen in full daylight. Tycho thus showed conclusively that the body was so remote that the diameter of the earth bore an insignificant ratio to the star's distance. His success in this respect is the more noteworthy when we find that many other observers, who studied the same object, came to the erroneous conclusion that the new star was quite as near as the moon, or even much nearer. In fact, it may be said, that with regard to this object Tycho discovered everything which could possibly have been discovered in the days before telescopes were invented. He not only proved that the star's distance was

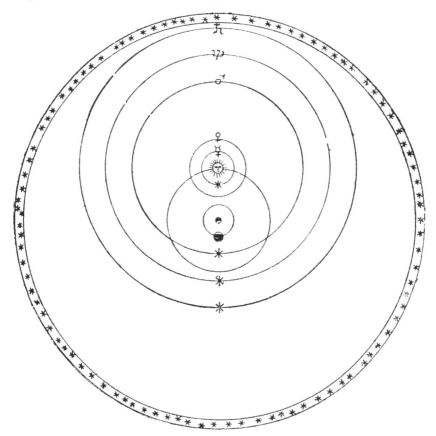

Tycho's "New Scheme of the Terrestrial System," 1577.

too great for measurement, but he showed that it had no proper motion on the heavens. He recorded the successive changes in its brightness from week to week, as well as the fluctuations in hue with which the alterations in lustre were accompanied.

It seems, nowadays, strange to find that such thoroughly scientific observations of the new star as those which Tycho made, possessed, even in the eyes of the great astronomer himself, a profound astrological significance. We learn from Dr. Dreyer that, in Tycho's opinion, "the star was at first like Venus and Jupiter, and its effects will therefore, first, be pleasant; but as it then became like Mars, there will next come a period of wars, seditions, captivity, and death of princes, and destruction of cities, together with dryness and fiery meteors in the air, pestilence, and venomous snakes. Lastly, the star became like Saturn, and

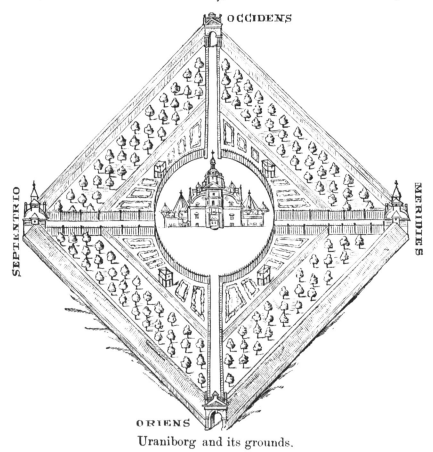

Uraniborg and its grounds.

thus will finally come a time of want, death, imprisonment, and all kinds of sad things!" Ideas of this kind were, however, universally entertained. It seemed, indeed, obvious to learned men of that period that such an apparition must forebode startling events. One of the chief theories then held was, that just as the Star of Bethlehem announced the first coming of Christ, so the second coming, and the end of the world, was heralded by the new star of 1572.

The researches of Tycho on this object were the occasion of his first appearance as an author. The publication of his book was however, for some time delayed by the urgent remonstrances of his friends, who thought it was beneath the dignity of a nobleman to condescend to write a book. Happily, Tycho determined to brave the opinion of his order; the book appeared, and was the first of a series of great astronomical productions from the same pen.

The fame of the noble Dane being now widespread, the King of Denmark entreated him to return to his native country, and to deliver a course of lectures on astronomy in the University of Copenhagen.

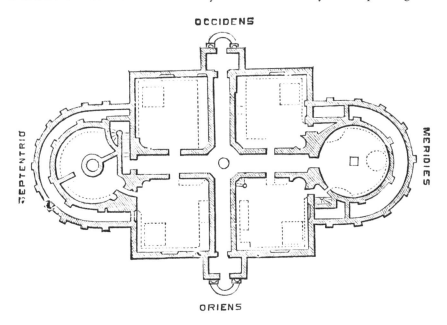

GROUND-PLAN OF THE OBSERVATORY.

With some reluctance he consented, and his introductory oration has been preserved. He dwells, in fervent language, upon the beauty and the interest of the celestial phenomena. He points out the imperative necessity of continuous and systematic observation of the heavenly bodies in order to extend our knowledge. He appeals to the practical utility of the science, for what civilised nation could exist without having the means of measuring time? He sets forth how the study of these beautiful objects "exalts the mind from earthly and trivial things to heavenly ones;" and then he winds up by assuring them that "a special use of astronomy is that it enables us to draw conclusions from the movements in the celestial regions as to human fate."

An interesting event, which occurred in 1572, distracted Tycho's attention from astronomical matters. He fell in love. The young girl on whom his affections were set appears to have sprung from humble origin. Here again his august family friends sought to dissuade him from a match they thought unsuitable for a nobleman. But Tycho never gave way in anything. It is suggested that he did not seek a wife among the highborn dames of his own rank from the dread that the demands

THE OBSERVATORY OF URANIBORG, ISLAND OF HVEN.

of a fashionable lady would make too great an inroad on the time that he wished to devote to science. At all events, Tycho's union seems to have been a happy one, and he had a large family of children; none of whom, however, inherited their father's talents.

Tycho had many scientific friends in Germany, among whom his work was held in high esteem. The treatment that he there met with seemed to him so much more encouraging than that which he received in Denmark that he formed the notion of emigrating to Basle and making it his permanent abode. A whisper of this intention was conveyed to the large-hearted King of Denmark, Frederick II. He wisely realised how great would be the fame which would accrue to his realm if he could induce Tycho to remain within Danish territory and carry on there the great work of his life. A resolution to make a splendid proposal to Tycho was immediately formed. A noble youth was forthwith despatched as a messenger, and ordered to travel day and night until he reached Tycho, whom he was to summon to the king. The astronomer was in bed on the morning of 11th February, 1576, when the message was delivered. Tycho, of course, set off at once and had an audience of the king at Copenhagen. The astronomer explained that what he wanted was the means to pursue his studies unmolested, whereupon the king offered him the Island of Hven, in the Sound near Elsinore. There he would enjoy all the seclusion that he could desire. The king further promised that he would provide the funds necessary for building a house and for founding the greatest observatory that had ever yet been reared for the study of the heavens. Af-ter due deliberation and consul-

EFFIGY ON TYCHO'S TOMB AT PRAGUE.

tation with his friends, Tycho accepted the king's offer. He was forthwith granted a pension, and a deed was drawn up formally assigning the Island of Hven to his use all the days of his life.

The foundation of the famous castle of Uraniborg was laid on 30th August, 1576. The ceremony was a formal and imposing one, in accordance with Tycho's ideas of splendour. A party of scientific friends had assembled, and the time had been chosen so that the heavenly bodies were auspiciously placed. Libations of costly wines were poured forth, and the stone was placed with due solemnity. The picturesque character of this wonderful temple for the study of the stars may be seen in the figures with which this chapter is illustrated.

One of the most remarkable instruments that has ever been employed in studying the heavens was the mural quadrant which Tycho erected in one of the apartments of Uraniborg. By its means the altitudes of the celestial bodies could be observed with much greater accuracy than had been previously attainable. This wonderful contrivance is represented on the preceding page. It will be observed that the walls of the room are adorned by pictures with a lavishness of decoration not usually to be found in scientific establishments.

A few years later, when the fame of the observatory at Hven became more widely spread, a number of young men flocked to Tycho to study under his direction. He therefore built another observatory for their use in which the instruments were placed in subterranean rooms of which only the roofs appeared above the ground. There was a wonderful poetical inscription over the entrance to this underground observatory, expressing the astonishment of Urania at finding, even in the interior of the earth, a cavern devoted to the study of the heavens. Tycho was indeed always fond of versifying, and he lost no opportunity of indulging this taste whenever an occasion presented itself.

Around the walls of the subterranean observatory were the pictures of eight astronomers, each with a suitable inscription—one of these of course represented Tycho himself, and beneath were written words to the effect that posterity should judge of his work. The eighth picture depicted an astronomer who has not yet come into existence. Tychonides was his name, and the inscription presses the modest hope that when he does appear he will be worthy of his great predecessor. The vast expenses incurred in the erection and the maintenance of this strange establishment were defrayed by a succession of grants from the royal purse.

For twenty years Tycho laboured hard at Uraniborg in the pursuit of science. His work mainly consisted in the determination of the places of the moon, the planets, and the stars on the celestial sphere. The extraordinary pains taken by Tycho to have his observations as accurate as his instruments would permit, have justly entitled him to the admiration of all succeeding astronomers. His island home provided the means of recreation as well as a place for work. He was surrounded

Tᴜᴄʜᴏ's Mᴜʀᴀʟ Qᴜᴀᴅʀᴀɴᴛ Pɪᴄᴛᴜʀᴇ, Uʀᴀɴɪʙᴏʀɢ.

by his family, troops of friends were not wanting, and a pet dwarf seems to have been an inmate of his curious residence. By way of change from his astronomical labours he used frequently to work with his students in his chemical laboratory. It is not indeed known what particular problems in chemistry occupied his attention. We are told, however, that he engaged largely in the production of medicines, and as these appear to have been dispensed gratuitously there was no lack of patients.

Tycho's imperious and grasping character frequently brought him into difficulties, which seem to have increased with his advancing years. He had ill-treated one of his tenants on Hven, and an adverse decision by the courts seems to have greatly exasperated the astronomer. Serious changes also took place in his relations to the court at Copenhagen. When the young king was crowned in 1596, he reversed the policy of his predecessor with reference to Hven. The liberal allowances to Tycho were one after another withdrawn, and finally even his pension was stopped. Tycho accordingly abandoned Hven in a tumult of rage and mortification. A few years later we find him in Bohemia a prematurely aged man, and he died on the 24th October, 1601.

GALILEO.

Among the ranks of the great astronomers it would be difficult to find one whose life presents more interesting features and remarkable vicissitudes than does that of Galileo. We may consider him as the patient investigator and brilliant discoverer. We may consider him in his private relations, especially to his daughter, Sister Maria Celeste, a woman of very remarkable character; and we have also the pathetic drama at the close of Galileo's life, when the philosopher drew down upon himself the thunders of the Inquisition.

The materials for the sketch of this astonishing man are sufficiently abundant. We make special use in this place of those charming letters which his daughter wrote to him from her convent home. More than a hundred of these have been preserved, and it may well be doubted whether any more beautiful and touching series of letters addressed to a parent by a dearly loved child have ever been written. An admirable account of this correspondence is contained in a little book entitled "The Private Life of Galileo," published anonymously by Messrs. Macmillan in 1870, and I have been much indebted to the author of that volume for many of the facts contained in this chapter.

Galileo was born at Pisa, on 18th February, 1564. He was the eldest son of Vincenzo de' Bonajuti de' Galilei, a Florentine noble. Notwithstanding his illustrious birth and descent, it would seem that the home in which the great philosopher's childhood was spent was an impoverished one. It was obvious at least that the young Galileo would have to be provided with some profession by which he might earn a livelihood. From his father he derived both by inheritance and by precept a keen taste for music, and it appears that he became an excellent performer on the lute. He was also endowed with considerable artistic power, which he cultivated diligently. Indeed, it would seem that for some time the future astronomer entertained the idea of devoting himself to painting as a profession. His father, however, decided that he should study medicine. Accordingly, we find that when Galileo was seventeen years of age, and had added a knowledge of Greek and Latin to his acquaintance with the fine arts, he was duly entered at the University of Pisa.

Here the young philosopher obtained some inkling of mathematics, whereupon he became so much interested in this branch of science, that he begged to be allowed to study geometry. In compliance with his request, his father permitted a tutor to be engaged for this purpose; but he did so with reluctance, fearing that the attention of the young student might thus be withdrawn from that medical work which was regarded as his primary occupation. The event speedily proved that these anxieties were not without some justification. The propositions of Euclid proved so engrossing to Galileo that it was thought wise to avoid further distraction by terminating the mathematical tutor's engagement. But it was too late for the desired end to be attained. Galileo had now made such progress that he was able to continue his geometrical studies by himself. Presently he advanced to that famous 47th proposition which won his lively admiration, and on he went until he had mastered the six books of Euclid, which was a considerable achievement for those days.

The diligence and brilliance of the young student at Pisa did not, however, bring him much credit with the University authorities. In those days the doctrines of Aristotle were regarded as the embodiment of all human wisdom in natural science as well as in everything else. It was regarded as the duty of every student to learn Aristotle off by heart, and any disposition to doubt or even to question the doctrines of the venerated teacher was regarded as intolerable presumption. But young Galileo had the audacity to think for himself about the laws of nature. He would not take any assertion of fact on the authority of Aristotle when he had the means of questioning nature directly as to its truth or falsehood. His teachers thus came to regard him as a somewhat misguided youth, though they could not but respect the unflagging industry with which he amassed all the knowledge he could acquire.

We are so accustomed to the use of pendulums in our clocks that

GALILEO'S PENDULUM.

perhaps we do not often realise that the introduction of this method of regulating time-pieces was really a notable invention worthy the fame of the great astronomer to whom it was due. It appears that sitting one day in the Cathedral of Pisa, Galileo's attention became concentrated on the swinging of a chandelier which hung from the ceiling. It struck him as a significant point, that whether the arc through which the pendulum oscillated was a long one or a short one, the time occupied in each vibration was sensibly the same. This suggested to the thoughtful observer that a pendulum would afford the means by which a time-keeper might be controlled, and accordingly Galileo constructed for the first time a clock on this principle. The immediate object sought in this apparatus was to provide a means of aiding physicians in counting the pulses of their patients.

The talents of Galileo having at length extorted due recognition from the authorities, he was appointed, at the age of twenty-five, Professor of Mathematics at the University of Pisa. Then came the time when he felt himself strong enough to throw down the gauntlet to the adherents of the old philosophy. As a necessary part of his doctrine on the movement of bodies Aristotle had asserted that the time occupied by a stone in falling depends upon its weight, so that the heavier the stone the less time would it require to fall from a certain height to the earth. It might have been thought that a statement so easily confuted by the simplest experiments could never have maintained its position in any accepted scheme of philosophy. But Aristotle had said it, and to anyone who ventured to express a doubt the ready sneer was forthcoming, "Do you think yourself a cleverer man than Aristotle?" Galileo determined to demonstrate in the most emphatic manner the absurdity of a doctrine which had for centuries received the sanction of the learned. The summit of the Leaning Tower of Pisa offered a highly dramatic site for the great experiment. The youthful professor let fall from the overhanging top a large heavy body and a small light body simultaneously. According to Aristotle the large body ought to have reached the ground much sooner than the small one, but such was found not to be the case. In the sight of a large concourse of people the simple fact was demonstrated that the two bodies fell side by side, and reached the ground at the same time. Thus the first great step was taken in the overthrow of that preposterous system of unquestioning adhesion to dogma, which had impeded the development of the knowledge of nature for nearly two thousand years.

This revolutionary attitude towards the ancient beliefs was not calculated to render Galileo's relations with the University authorities harmonious. He had also the misfortune to make enemies in other quarters. Don Giovanni de Medici, who was then the Governor of the Port of Leghorn, had designed some contrivance by which he proposed to pump out a dock. But Galileo showed up the absurdity of this enterprise in such an aggressive manner that Don Giovanni took mortal offence, nor was he mollified when the truths of Galileo's criticisms were abundantly verified by the total failure of his ridiculous inven-

PORTRAIT OF GALILEO.

tion. In various ways Galileo was made to feel his position at Pisa so unpleasant that he was at length compelled to abandon his chair in the University. The active exertions of his friends, of whom Galileo was so fortunate as to have had throughout his life an abundant supply, then secured his election to the Professorship of Mathematics at Padua, whither he went in 1592.

It was in this new position that Galileo entered on that marvellous career of investigation which was destined to revolutionize science. The zeal with which he discharged his professorial duties was indeed of the most unremitting character. He speedily drew such crowds to listen to his discourses on Natural Philosophy that his lecture-room was filled to overflowing. He also received many private pupils in his house for special instruction. Every moment that could be spared from these labours was devoted to his private study and to his incessant experiments.

Like many another philosopher who has greatly extended our knowledge of nature, Galileo had a remarkable aptitude for the invention of instruments designed for philosophical research. To facilitate his practical work, we find that in 1599 he had engaged a skilled workman who was to live in his house, and thus be constantly at hand to try the devices for ever springing from Galileo's fertile brain. Among the earliest of his inventions appears to have been the thermometer, which he constructed in 1602. No doubt this apparatus in its primitive form differed in some respects from the contrivance we call by the same name. Galileo at first employed water as the agent, by the expansion of which the temperature was to be measured. He afterwards saw the advantage of using spirits for the same purpose. It was not until about half a century later that mercury came to be recognised as the liquid most generally suitable for the thermometer.

The time was now approaching when Galileo was to make that mighty step in the advancement of human knowledge which followed on the application of the telescope to astronomy. As to how his idea of such an instrument originated, we had best let him tell us in his own words. The passage is given in a letter which he writes to his brother-in-law, Landucci.

"I write now because I have a piece of news for you, though whether you will be glad or sorry to hear it I cannot say; for I have now no hope of returning to my own country, though the occurrence which has destroyed that hope has had results both useful and honourable. You must know, then, that two months ago there was a report spread here that in Flanders some one had presented to Count Maurice of Nassau a glass manufactured in such a way as to make distant objects appear very near, so that a man at the distance of two miles could be clearly seen. This seemed to me so marvellous that I began to think about it. As it appeared to me to have a foundation in the Theory of Perspective, I set about contriving how to make it, and at length I found out, and have succeeded so well that the one I have made is far superior to the

Dutch telescope. It was reported in Venice that I had made one, and a week since I was commanded to show it to his Serenity and to all the members of the senate, to their infinite amazement. Many gentlemen and senators, even the oldest, have ascended at various times the highest bell-towers in Venice to spy out ships at sea making sail for the mouth of the harbour, and have seen them clearly, though without my telescope they would have been invisible for more than two hours. The effect of this instrument is to show an object at a distance of say fifty miles, as if it were but five miles."

The remarkable properties of the telescope at once commanded universal attention among intellectual men. Galileo received applications from several quarters for his new instrument, of which it would seem that he manufactured a large number to be distributed as gifts to various illustrious personages.

But it was reserved for Galileo himself to make that application of the instrument to the celestial bodies by which its peculiar powers were to inaugurate the new era in astronomy. The first discovery that was made in this direction appears to have been connected with the number of the stars. Galileo saw to his amazement that through his little tube he could count ten times as many stars in the sky as his unaided eye could detect. Here was, indeed, a surprise. We are now so familiar with the elementary facts of astronomy that it is not always easy to realise how the heavens were interpreted by the observers in those ages prior to the invention of the telescope. We can hardly, indeed, suppose that Galileo, like the majority of those who ever thought of such matters, entertained the erroneous belief that the stars were on the surface of a sphere at equal distances from the observer. No one would be likely to have retained his belief in such a doctrine when he saw how the number of visible stars could be increased tenfold by means of Galileo's telescope. It would have been almost impossible to refuse to draw the inference that the stars thus brought into view were still more remote objects which the telescope was able to reveal, just in the same way as it showed certain ships to the astonished Venetians, when at the time these ships were beyond the reach of unaided vision.

Galileo's celestial discoveries now succeeded each other rapidly. That beautiful Milky Way, which has for ages been the object of admiration to all lovers of nature, never disclosed its true nature to the eye of man till the astronomer of Padua turned on it his magic tube. The splendid zone of silvery light was then displayed as star-dust scattered over the black background of the sky. It was observed that though the individual stars were too small to be seen severally without optical aid, yet such was their incredible number that the celestial radiance produced that luminosity with which every stargazer was so familiar.

But the greatest discovery made by the telescope in these early days, perhaps, indeed, the greatest discovery that the telescope has ever accomplished, was the detection of the system of four satellites revolving around the great planet Jupiter. This phenomenon was so wholly unexpected by Galileo that, at first, he could hardly believe his eyes. However, the reality of the existence of a system of four moons attending the great planet was soon established beyond all question. Numbers of great personages crowded to Galileo to see for themselves this beautiful miniature representing the sun with its system of revolving planets.

Of course there were, as usual, a few incredulous people who refused to believe the assertion that four more moving bodies had to be added to the planetary system. They scoffed at the notion; they said the satellites may have been in the telescope, but that they were not in the sky. One sceptical philosopher is reported to have affirmed, that even if he saw the moons of Jupiter himself he would not believe in them, as their existence was contrary to the principles of common-sense!

There can be no doubt that a special significance attached to the new discovery at this particular epoch in the history of science. It must be remembered that in those days the doctrine of Copernicus, declaring that the sun, and not the earth, was the centre of the system, that the earth revolved on its axis once a day, and that it described a mighty circle round the sun once a year, had only recently been promulgated. This new view of the scheme of nature had been encountered with the most furious opposition. It may possibly have been that Galileo himself had not felt quite confident in the soundness of the Copernican theory, prior to the discovery of the satellites of Jupiter. But when a picture was there exhibited in which a number of relatively small globes were shown to be revolving around a single large globe in the centre, it seemed impossible not to feel that the beautiful spectacle so displayed was an emblem of the relations of the planets to the sun. It was thus made manifest to Galileo that the Copernican theory of the planetary system must be the true one. The momentous import of this opinion upon the future welfare of the great philosopher will presently appear.

It would seem that Galileo regarded his residence at Padua as a state of undesirable exile from his beloved Tuscany. He had always a yearning to go back to his own country and at last the desired opportunity presented itself. For now that Galileo's fame had become so great, the Grand Duke of Tuscany desired to have the philosopher resident at Florence, in the belief that he would shed lustre on the Duke's dominions. Overtures were accordingly made to Galileo, and the consequence was that in 1616 we find him residing at Florence, bearing the title of Mathematician and Philosopher to the Grand Duke.

Two daughters, Polissena and Virginia, and one son, Vincenzo, had been born to Galileo in Padua. It was the custom in those days that as soon as the daughter of an Italian gentleman had grown up, her future career was somewhat summarily decided. Either a husband was to be forthwith sought out, or she was to enter the convent with the object of taking the veil as a professed nun. It was arranged that the two daughters of Galileo, while still scarcely more than children, should both enter the Franciscan convent of St. Matthew, at Arcetri. The elder daughter Polissena, took the name of Sister Maria Celeste, while Virginia became Sister Arcangela. The latter seems to have been always delicate and subject to prolonged melancholy, and she is of but little account in the narrative of the life of Galileo. But Sister Maria Celeste, though never leaving the convent, managed to preserve a close intimacy with her beloved father. This was maintained only partly by Galileo's visits, which were very irregular and were, indeed, often suspended for long intervals. But his letters to this daughter were evidently frequent and affectionate, especially in the latter part of his life. Most unfortunately, however, all his letters have been lost. There are grounds for believing that they were deliberately destroyed when Galileo was seized by the Inquisition, lest they should have been used as evidence against him, or lest they should have compromised the convent where they were received. But Sister Maria Celeste's letters to her father have happily been preserved, and most touching these letters are. We can hardly read them without thinking how the sweet and gentle nun would have shrunk from the idea of their publication.

Her loving little notes to her "dearest lord and father," as she used affectionately to call Galileo, were almost invariably accompanied by some gift, trifling it may be, but always the best the poor nun had to bestow. The tender grace of these endearing communications was all the more precious to him from the fact that the rest of Galileo's relatives were of quite a worthless description. He always acknowledged the ties of his kindred in the most generous way, but their follies and their vices, their selfishness and their importunities, were an incessant source of annoyance to him, almost to the last day of his life.

On 19th December, 1625, Sister Maria Celeste writes:—

"I send two baked pears for these days of vigil. But as the greatest treat of all, I send you a rose, which ought to please you extremely, seeing what a rarity it is at this season; and with the rose you must accept its thorns, which represent the bitter passion of our Lord, whilst the green leaves represent the hope we may entertain that through the same sacred passion we, having passed through the darkness of the short winter of our mortal life, may attain to the brightness and felicity of an eternal spring in heaven."

When the wife and children of Galileo's shiftless brother came to take up their abode in the philosopher's home, Sister Maria Celeste feels glad to think that her father has now some one who, however imperfectly, may fulfil the duty of looking after him. A graceful note on Christmas Eve accompanies her little gifts. She hopes that—

"In these holy days the peace of God may rest on him and all the house. The largest collar and sleeves I mean for Albertino, the other two for the two younger boys, the little dog for baby, and the cakes for everybody, except the spice-cakes, which are for you. Accept the good-will which would readily do much more."

The extraordinary forbearance with which Galileo continually placed his time, his purse, and his influence at the service of those who had repeatedly proved themselves utterly unworthy of his countenance, is thus commented on by the good nun.—

"Now it seems to me, dearest lord and father, that your lordship is walking in the right path, since you take hold of every occasion that presents itself to shower continual benefits on those who only repay you with ingratitude. This is an action which is all the more virtuous and perfect as it is the more difficult."

When the plague was raging in the neighbourhood, the loving daughter's solicitude is thus shown:—

"I send you two pots of electuary as a preventive against the plague. The one without the label consists of dried figs, walnuts, rue, and salt, mixed together with honey. A piece of the size of a walnut to be taken in the morning, fasting, with a little Greek wine."

The plague increasing still more, Sister Maria Celeste obtained with much difficulty, a small quantity of a renowned liqueur, made by Abbess Ursula, an exceptionally saintly nun. This she sends to her father with the words:—

THE VILLA ARCETRI.
Galileo's residence, where Milton visited him.

"I pray your lordship to have faith in this remedy. For if you have so much faith in my poor miserable prayers, much more may you have in those of such a holy person; indeed, through her merits you may feel sure of escaping all danger from the plague."

Whether Galileo took the remedy we do not know, but at all events he escaped the plague.

From Galileo's new home in Florence the telescope was again directed to the skies, and again did astounding discoveries reward the astronomer's labours. The great success which he had met with in studying Jupiter naturally led Galileo to look at Saturn. Here he saw a spectacle which was sufficiently amazing, though he failed to interpret it accurately. It was quite manifest that Saturn did not exhibit a simple circular disc like Jupiter, or like Mars. It seemed to Galileo as if the planet consisted of three bodies, a large globe in the centre, and a smaller one on each side. The enigmatical nature of the discovery led Galileo to announce it in an enigmatical manner. He published a string of letters which, when duly transposed, made up a sentence which affirmed that the planet Saturn was threefold. Of course we now know that this remarkable appearance of the planet was due to the two projecting portions of the ring. With the feeble power of Galileo's telescope, these seemed merely like small globes or appendages to the large central body.

The last of Galileo's great astronomical discoveries related to the libration of the moon. I think that the detection of this phenomenon shows his acuteness of observation more remarkably than does any one of his other achievements with the telescope. It is well known that the moon constantly keeps the same face turned towards the earth. When, however, careful measurements have been made with regard to the spots and marks on the lunar surface, it is found that there is a slight periodic variation which permits us to see now a little to the east or to the west, now a little to the north or to the south of the average lunar disc.

But the circumstances which make the career of Galileo so especially interesting from the biographer's point of view, are hardly so much the triumphs that he won as the sufferings that he endured. The sufferings and the triumphs were, however, closely connected, and it is fitting that we should give due consideration to what was perhaps the greatest drama in the history of science.

On the appearance of the immortal work of Copernicus, in which it was taught that the earth rotated on its axis, and that the earth, like the other planets, revolved round the sun, orthodoxy stood aghast. The Holy Roman Church submitted this treatise, which bore the name "De Revolutionibus Orbium Coelestium," to the Congregation of the Index. After due examination it was condemned as heretical in 1615. Galileo was suspected, on no doubt excellent grounds, of entertaining the objectionable views of Copernicus. He was accordingly privately summoned before Cardinal Bellarmine on 26th February

1616, and duly admonished that he was on no account to teach or to defend the obnoxious doctrines. Galileo was much distressed by this intimation. He felt it a serious matter to be deprived of the privilege of discoursing with his friends about the Copernican system, and of instructing his disciples in the principles of the great theory of whose truth he was perfectly convinced. It pained him, however, still more to think, devout Catholic as he was, that such suspicions of his fervent allegiance to his Church should ever have existed, as were implied by the words and monitions of Cardinal Bellarmine.

In 1616, Galileo had an interview with Pope Paul V., who received the great astronomer very graciously, and walked up and down with him in conversation for three-quarters of an hour. Galileo complained to his Holiness of the attempts made by his enemies to embarrass him with the authorities of the Church, but the Pope bade him be comforted. His Holiness had himself no doubts of Galileo's orthodoxy, and he assured him that the Congregation of the Index should give Galileo no further trouble so long as Paul V. was in the chair of St. Peter.

On the death of Paul V. in 1623, Maffeo Barberini was elected Pope, as Urban VIII. This new Pope, while a cardinal, had been an intimate friend of Galileo's, and had indeed written Latin verses in praise of the great astronomer and his discoveries. It was therefore not unnatural for Galileo to think that the time had arrived when, with the use of due circumspection, he might continue his studies and his writings, without fear of incurring the displeasure of the Church. Indeed, in 1624, one of Galileo's friends writing from Rome, urges Galileo to visit the city again, and added that—

"Under the auspices of this most excellent, learned, and benignant Pontiff, science must flourish. Your arrival will be welcome to his Holiness. He asked me if you were coming, and when, and in short, he seems to love and esteem you more than ever."

The visit was duly paid, and when Galileo returned to Florence, the Pope wrote a letter from which the following is an extract, commanding the philosopher to the good offices of the young Ferdinand, who had shortly before succeeded his father in the Grand Duchy of Tuscany.

"We find in Galileo not only literary distinction, but also the love of piety, and he is also strong in those qualities by which the pontifical good-will is easily obtained. And now, when he has been brought to this city to congratulate us on our elevation, we have very lovingly embraced him; nor can we suffer him to return to the country whither your liberality calls him, without an ample provision of pontifical love. And that you may know how dear he is to us, we have willed to give him this honourable testimonial of virtue and piety. And we further signify that every benefit which you shall confer upon him, imitating or even surpassing your father's liberality, will conduce to our gratification."

The favourable reception which had been accorded to him by Pope Urban VIII. seems to have led Galileo to expect that there might be some corresponding change in the attitude of the Papal authorities on the great question of the stability of the earth. He accordingly proceeded with the preparation of the chief work of his life, "The Dialogue of the two Systems." It was submitted for inspection by the constituted authorities. The Pope himself thought that, if a few conditions which he laid down were duly complied with, there could be no objection to the publication of the work. In the first place, the title of the book was to be so carefully worded as to show plainly that the Copernican doctrine was merely to be regarded as an hypothesis, and not as a scientific fact. Galileo was also instructed to conclude the book with special arguments which had been supplied by the Pope himself, and which appeared to his Holiness to be quite conclusive against the new doctrine of Copernicus.

Formal leave for the publication of the Dialogue was then given to Galileo by the Inquisitor General, and it was accordingly sent to the press. It might be thought that the anxieties of the astronomer about his book would then have terminated. As a matter of fact, they had not yet seriously begun. Riccardi, the Master of the Sacred Palace, having suddenly had some further misgivings, sent to Galileo for the manuscript while the work was at the printer's, in order that the doctrine it implied might be once again examined. Apparently, Riccardi had come to the conclusion that he had not given the matter sufficient attention, when the authority to go to press had been first and, perhaps, hastily given. Considerable delay in the issue of the book was the result of these further deliberations. At last, however, in June, 1632, Galileo's great work, "The Dialogue of the two Systems," was produced for the instruction of the world, though the occasion was fraught with ruin to the immortal author.

The book, on its publication, was received and read with the greatest avidity. But presently the Master of The Sacred Palace found reason to regret that he had given his consent to its appearance. He accordingly issued a peremptory order to sequestrate every copy in Italy. This sudden change in the Papal attitude towards Galileo formed the sub-

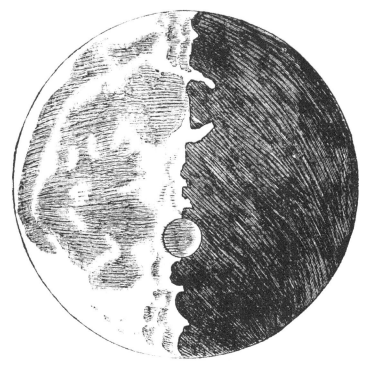

FACSIMILE SKETCH OF LUNAR SURFACE BY GALILEO.

ject of a strong remonstrance addressed to the Roman authorities by the Grand Duke of Tuscany. The Pope himself seemed to have become impressed all at once with the belief that the work contained matter of an heretical description. The general interpretation put upon the book seems to have shown the authorities that they had mistaken its true tendency, notwithstanding the fact that it had been examined again and again by theologians deputed for the duty. To the communication from the Grand Duke the Pope returned answer, that he had decided to submit the book to a congregation of "learned, grave, and saintly men," who would weigh every word in it. The views of his Holiness personally on the subject were expressed in his belief that the Dialogue contained the most perverse matter that could come into a reader's hands.

The Master of the Sacred Palace was greatly blamed by the authorities for having given his sanction to its issue. He pleaded that the book had not been printed in the precise terms of the original manuscript which had been submitted to him. It was also alleged that Galileo had not adhered to his promise of inserting properly the arguments which the Pope himself had given in support of the old and orthodox view. One of these had, no doubt, been introduced, but, so far from mending Galileo's case, it had made matters really look worse for the poor philosopher. The Pope's argument had been put into the mouth of one of the characters in the Dialogue named "Simplicio." Galileo's enemies maintained that by adopting such a method for the expression of his Holiness's opinion, Galileo had intended to hold the Pope himself up to ridicule. Galileo's friends maintained that nothing could have been farther from his intention. It seems, however, highly probable that the suspicions thus aroused had something to say to the sudden change of front on the part of the Papal authorities.

On 1st October, 1632, Galileo received an order to appear before the Inquisition at Rome on the grave charge of heresy. Galileo, of course, expressed his submission, but pleaded for a respite from compliance with the summons, on the ground of his advanced age and his failing health. The Pope was, however, inexorable; he said that he had warned Galileo of his danger while he was still his friend. The command could not be disobeyed. Galileo might perform the journey as slowly as he pleased, but it was imperatively necessary for him to set forth and at once.

On 20th January, 1633, Galileo started on his weary journey to Rome, in compliance with this peremptory summons. On 13th February he was received as the guest of Niccolini, the Tuscan ambassador, who had acted as his wise and ever-kind friend throughout the whole affair. It seemed plain that the Holy Office were inclined to treat Galileo with as much clemency and consideration as was consistent with the determination that the case against him should be proceeded with to the end. The Pope intimated that in consequence of his respect for the Grand Duke of Tuscany he should permit Galileo to enjoy the privilege, quite unprecedented for a prisoner charged with heresy, of remaining as an inmate in the ambassador's house. He ought, strictly, to have been placed in the dungeons of the Inquisition. When the examination of the accused had actually commenced, Galileo was confined, not, indeed, in the dungeons, but in comfortable rooms at the Holy Office.

By the judicious and conciliatory language of submission which Niccolini had urged Galileo to use before the Inquisitors, they were so far satisfied that they interceded with the Pope for his release. During the remainder of the trial Galileo was accordingly permitted to go back to the ambassador's, where he was most heartily welcomed. Sister Maria Celeste, evidently thinking this meant that the whole case was at an end, thus expresses herself:—

"The joy that your last dear letter brought me, and the having to read it over and over to the nuns, who made quite a jubilee on hearing its contents, put me into such an excited state that at last I got a severe attack of headache."

In his defence Galileo urged that he had already been acquitted in 1616 by Cardinal Bellarmine, when a charge of heresy was brought against him, and he contended that anything he might now have done, was no more than he had done on the preceding occasion, when the orthodoxy of his doctrines received solemn confirmation. The Inquisition seemed certainly inclined to clemency, but the Pope was not satisfied. Galileo was accordingly summoned again on the 21st June. He was to be threatened with torture if he did not forthwith give satisfactory explanations as to the reasons which led him to write the Dialogue. In this proceeding the Pope assured the Tuscan ambassador that he was treating Galileo with the utmost consideration possible in consequence of his esteem and regard for the Grand Duke, whose servant Galileo was. It was, however, necessary that some exemplary punishment be meted out to the astronomer, inasmuch as by the publication of the Dialogue he had distinctly disobeyed the injunction of silence laid upon him by the decree of 1616. Nor was it admissible for Galileo to plead that his book had been sanctioned by the Master of the Sacred College, to whose inspection it had been again and again submitted. It was held, that if the Master of the Sacred College had been unaware of the solemn warning the philosopher had already received sixteen years previously, it was the duty of Galileo to have drawn his attention to that fact.

On the 22nd June, 1633, Galileo was led to the great hall of the Inquisition, and compelled to kneel before the cardinals there assembled and hear his sentence. In a long document, most elaborately drawn up, it is definitely charged against Galileo that, in publishing the Dialogue, he committed the essentially grave error of treating the doctrine of the earth's motion as open to discussion. Galileo knew, so the document affirmed, that the Church had emphatically pronounced this notion to be contrary to Holy Writ, and that for him to consider a doctrine so stigmatized as having any shadow of probability in its favour was an act of disrespect to the authority of the Church which could not be overlooked. It was also charged against Galileo that in his Dialogue he has put the strongest arguments into the mouth, not of those who supported the orthodox doctrine, but of those who held the theory as to the earth's motion which the Church had so deliberately condemned.

After due consideration of the defence made by the prisoner, it was thereupon decreed that he had rendered himself vehemently suspected of heresy by the Holy Office, and in consequence had incurred all the censures and penalties of the sacred canons, and other decrees promulgated against such persons. The graver portion of these punishments would be remitted, if Galileo would solemnly repudiate the heresies referred to by an abjuration to be pronounced by him in the terms laid down.

At the same time it was necessary to mark, in some emphatic manner, the serious offence which had been committed, so that it might serve both as a punishment to Galileo and as a warning to others. It was accordingly decreed that he should be condemned to imprisonment in the Holy Office during the pleasure of the Papal authorities, and that he should recite once a week for three years the seven Penitential Psalms.

Then followed that ever-memorable scene in the great hall of the Inquisition, in which the aged and infirm Galileo, the inventor of the telescope and the famous astronomer, knelt down to abjure before the most eminent and reverend Lords Cardinal, Inquisitors General throughout the Christian Republic against heretical depravity. With his hands on the Gospels, Galileo was made to curse and detest the false opinion that the sun was the centre of the universe and immovable, and that the earth was not the centre of the same, and that it moved. He swore that for the future he will never say nor write such things as may bring him under suspicion, and that if he does so he submits to all the pains and penalties of the sacred canons. This abjuration was subsequently read in Florence before Galileo's disciples, who had been specially summoned to attend.

It has been noted that neither on the first occasion, in 1616, nor on the second in 1633, did the reigning Pope sign the decrees concerning Galileo. The contention has accordingly been made that Paul V. and Urban VIII. are both alike vindicated from any technical responsibility for the attitude of the Romish Church towards the Copernican doctrines. The significance of this circumstance has been commented on in connection with the doctrine of the infallibility of the Pope.

We can judge of the anxiety felt by Sister Maria Celeste about her beloved father during these terrible trials. The wife of the ambassador Niccolini, Galileo's steadfast friend, most kindly wrote to give the nun whatever quieting assurances the case would permit. There is a renewed flow of these touching epistles from the daughter to her father. Thus she sends word—

"The news of your fresh trouble has pierced my soul with grief all the more that it came quite unexpectedly."

And again, on hearing that he had been permitted to leave Rome, she writes—

"I wish I could describe the rejoicing of all the mothers and sisters on hearing of your happy arrival at Siena. It was indeed most extraordinary. On hearing the news the Mother Abbess and many of the nuns ran to me, embracing me and weeping for joy and tenderness."

The sentence of imprisonment was at first interpreted leniently by the Pope. Galileo was allowed to reside in qualified durance in the archbishop's house at Siena. Evidently the greatest pain that he endured arose from the forced separation from that daughter, whom he had at last learned to love with an affection almost comparable with that she bore to him. She had often told him that she never had any pleasure equal to that with which she rendered any service to her father. To her joy, she discovers that she can relieve him from the task of reciting the seven Penitential Psalms which had been imposed as a Penance:—

"I began to do this a while ago," she writes, "and it gives me much pleasure. First, because I am persuaded that prayer in obedience to Holy Church must be efficacious; secondly, in order to save you the trouble of remembering it. If I had been able to do more, most willingly would I have entered a straiter prison than the one I live in now, if by so doing I could have set you at liberty."

CREST OF GALILEO'S FAMILY.

Sister Maria Celeste was gradually failing in health, but the great privilege was accorded to her of being able once again to embrace her beloved lord and master. Galileo had, in fact, been permitted to return to his old home; but on the very day when he heard of his daughter's death came the final decree directing him to remain in his own house in perpetual solitude.

Amid the advancing infirmities of age, the isolation from friends, and the loss of his daughter, Galileo once again sought consolation in hard work. He commenced his famous dialogue on Motion. Gradually, however, his sight began to fail, and blindness was at last added to his other troubles. On January 2nd, 1638, he writes to Diodati:—

"Alas, your dear friend and servant, Galileo, has been for the last month perfectly blind, so that this heaven, this earth, this universe which I by my marvellous discoveries and clear demonstrations have enlarged a hundred thousand times beyond the belief of the wise men of bygone ages, henceforward is for me shrunk into such a small space as is filled by my own bodily sensations."

But the end was approaching—the great philosopher, was attacked by low fever, from which he died on the 8th January, 1643.

KEPLER.

While the illustrious astronomer, Tycho Brahe, lay on his death-
bed, he had an interview which must ever rank as one of the important
incidents in the history of science. The life of Tycho had been passed,
as we have seen, in the accumulation of vast stores of careful observations of the positions of the heavenly bodies. It was not given to him to
deduce from his splendid work the results to which they were destined
to lead. It was reserved for another astronomer to distil, so to speak,
from the volumes in which Tycho's figures were recorded, the great
truths of the universe which those figures contained. Tycho felt that
his work required an interpreter, and he recognised in the genius of a
young man with whom he was acquainted the agent by whom the
world was to be taught some of the great truths of nature. To the bed-
side of the great Danish astronomer the youthful philosopher was
summoned, and with his last breath Tycho besought of him to spare
no labour in the performance of those calculations, by which alone the
secrets of the movements of the heavens could be revealed. The solemn
trust thus imposed was duly accepted, and the man who accepted it
bore the immortal name of Kepler.

Kepler was born on the 27th December, 1571, at Weil, in the
Duchy of Wurtemberg. It would seem that the circumstances of his
childhood must have been singularly unhappy. His father, sprung
from a well-connected family, was but a shiftless and idle adventurer;
nor was the great astronomer much more fortunate in his other parent. His mother was an ignorant and ill-tempered woman; indeed, the
ill-assorted union came to an abrupt end through the desertion of the
wife by her husband when their eldest son John, the hero of our
present sketch, was eighteen years old. The childhood of this lad, des-

tined for such fame, was still further embittered by the circumstance that when he was four years old he had a severe attack of small-pox. Not only was his eyesight permanently injured, but even his constitution appears to have been much weakened by this terrible malady.

It seems, however, that the bodily infirmities of young John Kepler were the immediate cause of his attention being directed to the pursuit of knowledge. Had the boy been fitted like other boys for ordinary manual work, there can be hardly any doubt that to manual work his life must have been devoted. But, though his body was feeble, he soon gave indications of the possession of considerable mental power. It was accordingly thought that a suitable sphere for his talents might be found in the Church which, in those days, was almost the only profession that afforded an opening for an intellectual career. We thus find that by the time John Kepler was seventeen years old he had attained a sufficient standard of knowledge to entitle him to admission on the foundation of the University at Tubingen.

In the course of his studies at this institution he seems to have divided his attention equally between astronomy and divinity. It not unfrequently happens that when a man has attained considerable proficiency in two branches of knowledge he is not able to see very clearly in which of the two pursuits his true vocation lies. His friends and onlookers are often able to judge more wisely than he himself can do as to which of the two lines it would be better for him to pursue. This incapacity for perceiving the path in which greatness awaited him, existed in the case of Kepler. Personally, he inclined to enter the ministry, in which a promising career seemed open to him. He yielded, however, to friends, who evidently knew him better than he knew himself, and accepted in 1594, the important Professorship of astronomy which had been offered to him in the University of Gratz.

It is difficult for us in these modern days to realise the somewhat extraordinary duties which were expected from an astronomical professor in the sixteenth century. He was, of course, required to employ his knowledge of the heavens in the prediction of eclipses, and of the movements of the heavenly bodies generally. This seems reasonable enough; but what we are not prepared to accept is the obligation which lay on the astronomers to predict the fates of nations and the destinies of individuals.

It must be remembered that it was the almost universal belief in those days, that all the celestial spheres revolved in some mysterious fashion around the earth, which appeared by far the most important body in the universe. It was imagined that the sun, the moon, and the stars indicated, in the vicissitudes of their movements, the careers of nations and of individuals. Such being the generally accepted notion, it seemed to follow that a professor who was charged with the duty of expounding the movements of the heavenly bodies must necessarily be looked to for the purpose of deciphering the celestial decrees regarding the fate of man which the heavenly luminaries were designed to announce.

Kepler threw himself with characteristic ardour into even this fantastic phase of the labours of the astronomical professor; he diligently studied the rules of astrology, which the fancies of antiquity had compiled. Believing sincerely as he did in the connection between the aspect of the stars and the state of human affairs, he even thought that he perceived, in the events of his own life, a corroboration of the doctrine which affirmed the influence of the planets upon the fate of individuals.

But quite independently of astrology there seem to have been many other delusions current among the philosophers of Kepler's time. It is now almost incomprehensible how the ablest men of a few centuries ago should have entertained such preposterous notions, as they did, with respect to the system of the universe. As an instance of what is here referred to, we may cite the extraordinary notion which, under the designation of a discovery, first brought Kepler into fame. Geometers had long known that there were five, but no more than five, regular solid figures. There is, for instance, the cube with six sides, which is, of course, the most familiar of these solids. Besides the cube there are other figures of four, eight, twelve, and twenty sides respectively. It also happened that there were five planets, but no more than five, known to the ancients, namely, Mercury, Venus, Mars, Jupiter, and Saturn. To Kepler's lively imaginations this coincidence suggested the idea that the five regular solids corresponded to the five planets, and a number of fancied numerical relations were adduced on the subject. The absurdity of this doctrine is obvious enough, especially when we observe that, as is now well known, there are two large planets, and a host of

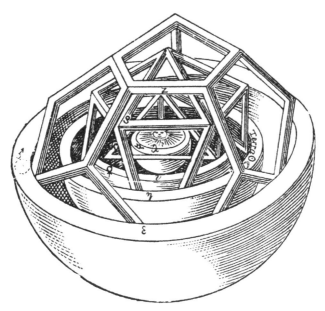

KEPLER'S SYSTEM OF REGULAR SOLIDS.

small planets, over and above the magical number of the regular solids. In Kepler's time, however, this doctrine was so far from being regarded as absurd, that its announcement was hailed as a great intellectual triumph. Kepler was at once regarded with favour. It seems, indeed, to have been the circumstance which brought him into correspondence with Tycho Brahe. By its means also he became known to Galileo.

The career of a scientific professor in those early days appears generally to have been marked by rather more striking vicissitudes than usually befall a professor in a modern university. Kepler was a Protestant, and as such he had been appointed to his professorship at Gratz. A change, however, having taken place in the religious belief entertained by the ruling powers of the University, the Protestant professors were expelled. It seems that special influence having been exerted in Kepler's case on account of his exceptional eminence, he was recalled to Gratz and reinstated in the tenure of his chair. But his pupils had vanished, so that the great astronomer was glad to accept a post offered him by Tycho Brahe in the observatory which the latter had recently established near Prague.

On Tycho's death, which occurred soon after, an opening presented itself which gave Kepler the opportunity his genius demanded.

He was appointed to succeed Tycho in the position of imperial mathematician. But a far more important point, both for Kepler and for science, was that to him was confided the use of Tycho's observations. It was, indeed, by the discussion of Tycho's results that Kepler was enabled to make the discoveries which form such an important part of astronomical history.

Kepler must also be remembered as one of the first great astronomers who ever had the privilege of viewing celestial bodies through a telescope. It was in 1610 that he first held in his hands one of those little instruments which had been so recently applied to the heavens by Galileo. It should, however, be borne in mind that the epoch-making achievements of Kepler did not arise from any telescopic observations that he made, or, indeed, that any one else made. They were all elaborately deduced from Tycho's measurements of the positions of the planets, obtained with his great instruments, which were unprovided with telescopic assistance.

To realise the tremendous advance which science received from Kepler's great work, it is to be understood that all the astronomers who laboured before him at the difficult subject of the celestial motions, took it for granted that the planets must revolve in circles. If it did not appear that a planet moved in a fixed circle, then the ready answer was provided by Ptolemy's theory that the circle in which the planet did move was itself in motion, so that its centre described another circle.

When Kepler had before him that wonderful series of observations of the planet, Mars, which had been accumulated by the extraordinary skill of Tycho, he proved, after much labour, that the movements of the planet refused to be represented in a circular form. Nor would it do to suppose that Mars revolved in one circle, the centre of which revolved in another circle. On no such supposition could the movements of the planets be made to tally with those which Tycho had actually observed. This led to the astonishing discovery of the true form of a planet's orbit. For the first time in the history of astronomy the principle was laid down that the movement of a planet could not be represented by a circle, nor even by combinations of circles, but that it could be represented by an elliptic path. In this path the sun is situated at one of those two points in the ellipse which are known as its foci.

Very simple apparatus is needed for the drawing of one of those ellipses which Kepler has shown to possess such astonishing astronomical significance. Two pins are stuck through a sheet of paper on a board, the point of a pencil is inserted in a loop of string which passes over the pins, and as the pencil is moved round in such a way as to keep

Kepler.

the string stretched, that beautiful curve known as the ellipse is delineated, while the positions of the pins indicate the two foci of the curve. If the length of the loop of string is unchanged then the nearer the pins are together, the greater will be the resemblance between the ellipse and the circle, whereas the more the pins are separated the more elongated does the ellipse become. The orbit of a great planet is, in general, one of those ellipses which approaches a nearly circular form. It fortunately happens, however, that the orbit of Mars makes a wider departure from the circular form than any of the other important planets. It is, doubtless, to this circumstance that we must attribute the astonishing success of Kepler in detecting the true shape of a planetary orbit. Tycho's observations would not have been sufficiently accurate to have exhibited the elliptic nature of a planetary orbit which, like that of Venus, differed very little from a circle.

The more we ponder on this memorable achievement the more striking will it appear. It must be remembered that in these days we know of the physical necessity which requires that a planet shall revolve in an ellipse and not in any other curve. But Kepler had no such knowledge. Even to the last hour of his life he remained in ignorance of the existence of any natural cause which ordained that planets should follow those particular curves which geometers know so well. Kepler's assignment of the ellipse as the true form of the planetary orbit is to be regarded as a brilliant guess, the truth of which Tycho's observations enabled him to verify. Kepler also succeeded in pointing out the law according to which the velocity of a planet at different points of its path could be accurately specified. Here, again, we have to admire the sagacity with which this marvellously acute astronomer guessed the deep truth of nature. In this case also he was quite unprovided with any reason for expecting from physical principles that such a law as he discovered must be obeyed. It is quite true that Kepler had some slight knowledge of the existence of what we now know as gravitation. He had even enunciated the remarkable doctrine that the ebb and flow of the tide must be attributed to the attraction of the moon on the waters of the earth. He does not, however, appear to have had any anticipation of those wonderful discoveries which Newton was destined to make a little later, in which he demonstrated that the laws detected by Kepler's marvellous acumen were necessary consequences of the principle of universal gravitation.

To appreciate the relations of Kepler and Tycho it is necessary to note the very different way in which these illustrious astronomers viewed the system of the heavens. It should be observed that Copernicus had already expounded the true system, which located the sun at

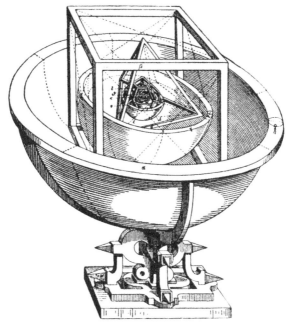

SYMBOLICAL REPRESENTATION OF THE PLANETARY SYSTEM.

the centre of the planetary system. But in the days of Tycho Brahe this doctrine had not as yet commanded universal assent. In fact, the great observer himself did not accept the new views of Copernicus. It appeared to Tycho that the earth not only appeared to be the centre of things celestial, but that it actually was the centre. It is, indeed, not a little remarkable that a student of the heavens so accurate as Tycho should have deliberately rejected the Copernican doctrine in favour of the system which now seems so preposterous. Throughout his great career, Tycho steadily observed the places of the sun, the moon, and the planets, and as steadily maintained that all those bodies revolved around the earth fixed in the centre. Kepler, however, had the advantage of belonging to the new school. He utilised the observations of Tycho in developing the great Copernican theory whose teaching Tycho stoutly resisted.

Perhaps a chapter in modern science may illustrate the intellectual relation of these great men. The revolution produced by Copernicus in the doctrine of the heavens has often been likened to the revolution which the Darwinian theory produced in the views held by biologists as to life on this earth. The Darwinian theory did not at first command universal assent even among those naturalists whose lives had been devoted with the greatest success to the study of organisms. Take, for instance, that great naturalist, Professor Owen, by whose labours vast extension has been given to our knowledge of the fossil animals which dwelt on the earth in past ages. Now, though Owens researches were intimately connected with the great labours of Darwin, and afforded the latter material for his epoch-making generalization, yet Owen deliberately refused to accept the new doctrines. Like Tycho, he kept on rigidly accumulating his facts under the influence of a set of ideas as to the origin of living forms which are now universally admitted to be erroneous. If, therefore, we liken Darwin to Copernicus, and Owen to Tycho, we may liken the biologists of the present day to Kepler, who interpreted the results of accurate observation upon sound theoretical principles.

In reading the works of Kepler in the light of our modern knowledge we are often struck by the extent to which his perception of the sublimest truths in nature was associated with the most extravagant errors and absurdities. But, of course, it must be remembered that he wrote in an age in which even the rudiments of science, as we now understand it, were almost entirely unknown.

It may well be doubted whether any joy experienced by mortals is more genuine than that which rewards the successful searcher after natural truths. Every science-worker, be his efforts ever so humble, will be able to sympathise with the enthusiastic delight of Kepler when at last, after years of toil, the glorious light broke forth, and that which he considered to be the greatest of his astonishing laws first dawned upon him. Kepler rightly judged that the number of days which a planet required to perform its voyage round the sun must be connected in some manner with the distance from the planet to the sun; that is to say, with the radius of the planet's orbit, inasmuch as we may for our present object regard the planet's orbit as circular.

Here, again, in his search for the unknown law, Kepler had no accurate dynamical principles to guide his steps. Of course, we now know not only what the connection between the planet's distance and the planet's periodic time actually is, but we also know that it is a necessary consequence of the law of universal gravitation. Kepler, it is true, was not without certain surmises on the subject, but they were of the most fanciful description. His notions of the planets, accurate as they were in certain important respects, were mixed up with vague ideas as to the properties of metals and the geometrical relations of the regular solids. Above all, his reasoning was penetrated by the supposed astrological influences of the stars and their significant relation to human fate. Under the influence of such a farrago of notions, Kepler resolved to make all sorts of trials in his search for the connection between the distance of a planet from the sun and the time in which the revolution of that planet was accomplished.

It was quite easily demonstrated that the greater the distance of the planet from the sun the longer was the time required for its journey. It might have been thought that the time would be directly proportional to the distance. It was, however, easy to show that this supposition did not agree with the fact. Finding that this simple relation would not do, Kepler undertook a vast series of calculations to find out the true method of expressing the connection. At last, after many vain attempts, he found, to his indescribable joy, that the square of the time in which a planet revolves around the sun was proportional to the cube of the average distance of the planet from that body.

The extraordinary way in which Kepler's views on celestial matters were associated with the wildest speculations, is well illustrated in the work in which he propounded his splendid discovery just referred to. The announcement of the law connecting the distances of the planets from the sun with their periodic times, was then mixed up with a preposterous conception about the properties of the different planets. They were supposed to be associated with some profound music of the spheres inaudible to human ears, and performed only for the benefit of that being whose soul formed the animating spirit of the sun.

Kepler was also the first astronomer who ever ventured to predict the occurrence of that remarkable phenomenon, the transit of a planet in front of the sun's disc. He published, in 1629, a notice to the curious in things celestial, in which he announced that both of the planets, Mercury and Venus, were to make a transit across the sun on specified days in the winter of 1631. The transit of Mercury was duly observed by Gassendi, and the transit of Venus also took place, though, as we now know, the circumstances were such that it was not possible for the phenomenon to be witnessed by any European astronomer.

In addition to Kepler's discoveries already mentioned, with which his name will be for ever associated, his claim on the gratitude of astronomers chiefly depends on the publication of his famous Rudolphine tables. In this remarkable work means are provided for finding the places of the planets with far greater accuracy than had previously been attainable.

Kepler, it must be always remembered, was not an astronomical observer. It was his function to deal with the observations made by Tycho, and, from close study and comparison of the results, to work out the movements of the heavenly bodies. It was, in fact, Tycho who provided as it were the raw material, while it was the genius of Kepler which wrought that material into a beautiful and serviceable form. For more than a century the Rudolphine tables were regarded as a standard astronomical work. In these days we are accustomed to find the movements of the heavenly bodies set forth with all desirable exactitude in the *Nautical Almanack*, and the similar publication issued by foreign Governments. Let it be remembered that it was Kepler who first imparted the proper impulse in this direction.

When Kepler was twenty-six he married an heiress from Styria, who, though only twenty-three years old, had already had some experience in matrimony. Her first husband had died; and it was after her second husband had divorced her that she received the addresses of Kepler. It will not be surprising to hear that his domestic affairs do not appear to have been particularly happy, and his wife died in 1611. Two years later, undeterred by the want of success in his first venture, he sought a second partner, and he evidently determined not to make a mistake this time. Indeed, the methodical manner in which he made his choice of the lady to whom he should propose has been duly set forth by him and preserved for our edification. With some self-assurance he asserts that there were no fewer than eleven spinsters desirous of sharing his joys and sorrows. He has carefully estimated and recorded the merits and demerits of each of these would-be brides. The result of his deliberations was that he awarded himself to an orphan girl, destitute even of a portion. Success attended his choice, and his second marriage

THE COMMEMORATION OF THE RUDOLPHINE TABLE.

seems to have proved a much more suitable union than his first. He had five children by the first wife and seven by the second.

The years of Kepler's middle life were sorely distracted by a trouble which, though not uncommon in those days, is one which we find it difficult to realise at the present time. His mother, Catherine Kepler, had attained undesirable notoriety by the suspicion that she was guilty of witchcraft. Years were spent in legal investigations, and it was only after unceasing exertions on the part of the astronomer for upwards of a twelve-month that he was finally able to procure her acquittal and release from prison.

It is interesting for us to note that at one time there was a proposal that Kepler should forsake his native country and adopt England as a home. It arose in this wise. The great man was distressed throughout the greater part of his life by pecuniary anxieties. Finding him in a strait of this description, the English ambassador in Venice, Sir Henry Wotton, in the year 1620, besought Kepler to come over to England, where he assured him that he would obtain a favourable reception, and where, he was able to add, Kepler's great scientific work was already highly esteemed. But his efforts were unavailing; Kepler would not leave his own country. He was then forty-nine years of age, and doubtless a home in a foreign land, where people spoke a strange tongue, had not sufficient attraction for him, even when accompanied with the substantial inducements which the ambassador was able to offer. Had Kepler accepted this invitation, he would, in transferring his home to England, have anticipated the similar change which took place in the career of another great astronomer two centuries later. It will be remembered that Herschel, in his younger days, did transfer himself to England, and thus gave to England the imperishable fame of association with his triumphs.

The publication of the Rudolphine tables of the celestial movements entailed much expense. A considerable part of this was defrayed by the Government at Venice but the balance occasioned no little trouble and anxiety to Kepler. No doubt the authorities of those days were even less willing to spend money on scientific matters than are the Governments of more recent times. For several years the imperial Treasury was importuned to relieve him from his anxieties. The effects of so much worry, and of the long journeys which were involved, at last broke down Kepler's health completely. As we have already mentioned, he had never been strong from infancy, and he finally succumbed to a fever in November, 1630, at the age of fifty-nine. He was interred at St. Peter's Church at Ratisbon.

Though Kepler had not those personal characteristics which have made his great predecessor, Tycho Brahe, such a romantic figure, yet a picturesque element in Kepler's character is not wanting. It was, however, of an intellectual kind. His imagination, as well as his reasoning faculties, always worked together. He was incessantly prompted by the most extraordinary speculations. The great majority of them were in a high degree wild and chimerical, but every now and then one of his fancies struck right to the heart of nature, and an immortal truth was brought to light.

I remember visiting the observatory of one of our greatest modern astronomers, and in a large desk he showed me a multitude of photographs which he had attempted but which had not been successful, and then he showed me the few and rare pictures which had succeeded, and by which important truths had been revealed. With a felicity of expression which I have often since thought of, he alluded to the contents of the desk as the "chips." They were useless, but they were necessary incidents in the truly successful work. So it is in all great and good work. Even the most skilful man of science pursues many a wrong scent. Time after time he goes off on some track that plays him false. The greater the man's genius and intellectual resource, the more numerous will be the ventures which he makes, and the great majority of those ventures are certain to be fruitless. They are in fact, the "chips." In Kepler's case the chips were numerous enough. They were of the most extraordinary variety and structure. But every now and then a sublime discovery was made of such a character as to make us regard even the most fantastic of Kepler's chips with the greatest veneration and respect.

ISAAC NEWTON.

It was just a year after the death of Galileo, that an infant came into the world who was christened Isaac Newton. Even the great fame of Galileo himself must be relegated to a second place in comparison with that of the philosopher who first expounded the true theory of the universe.

Isaac Newton was born on the 25th of December (old style), 1642, at Woolsthorpe, in Lincolnshire, about a half-mile from Colsterworth, and eight miles south of Grantham. His father, Mr. Isaac Newton, had died a few months after his marriage to Harriet Ayscough, the daughter of Mr. James Ayscough, of Market Overton, in Rutlandshire. The little Isaac was at first so excessively frail and weakly that his life was despaired of. The watchful mother, however, tended her delicate child with such success that he seems to have thriven better than might have been expected from the circumstances of his infancy, and he ultimately acquired a frame strong enough to outlast the ordinary span of human life.

For three years they continued to live at Woolsthorpe, the widow's means of livelihood being supplemented by the income from another small estate at Sewstern, in a neighbouring part of Leicestershire.

In 1645, Mrs. Newton took as a second husband the Rev. Barnabas Smith, and on moving to her new home, about a mile from Woolsthorpe, she entrusted little Isaac to her mother, Mrs. Ayscough. In due time we find that the boy was sent to the public school at Grantham, the name of the master being Stokes. For the purpose of being near his work, the embryo philosopher was boarded at the house of Mr. Clark, an apothecary at Grantham. We learn from Newton himself that at first he had a very low place in the class lists of the

school, and was by no means one of those model school-boys who find
favour in the eyes of the school-master by attention to Latin grammar.
Isaac's first incentive to diligent study seems to have been derived from
the circumstance that he was severely kicked by one of the boys who
was above him in the class. This indignity had the effect of stimulating
young Newton's activity to such an extent that he not only attained
the desired object of passing over the head of the boy who had mal-
treated him, but continued to rise until he became the head of the
school.

The play-hours of the great philosopher were devoted to pursuits
very different from those of most school-boys. His chief amusement
was found in making mechanical toys and various ingenious con-

WOOLSTHORPE MANOR.
Showing solar dial made by Newton when a boy.

trivances. He watched day by day with great interest the workmen engaged in constructing a windmill in the neighbourhood of the school,
the result of which was that the boy made a working model of the
windmill and of its machinery, which seems to have been much ad-
mired, as indicating his aptitude for mechanics. We are told that Isaac
also indulged in somewhat higher flights of mechanical enterprise. He
constructed a carriage, the wheels of which were to be driven by the
hands of the occupant, while the first philosophical instrument he
made was a clock, which was actuated by water. He also devoted much
attention to the construction of paper kites, and his skill in this respect
was highly appreciated by his school-fellows. Like a true philosopher,

even at this stage he experimented on the best methods of attaching the string, and on the proportions which the tail ought to have. He also made lanthorns of paper to provide himself with light as he walked to school in the dark winter mornings.

The only love affair in Newton's life appears to have commenced while he was still of tender years. The incidents are thus described in Brewster's "Life of Newton," a work to which I am much indebted in this chapter.

"In the house where he lodged there were some female inmates, in whose company he appears to have taken much pleasure. One of these, a Miss Storey, sister to Dr. Storey, a physician at Buckminster, near Colsterworth, was two or three years younger than Newton and to great personal attractions she seems to have added more than the usual allotment of female talent. The society of this young lady and her companions was always preferred to that of his own school-fellows, and it was one of his most agreeable occupations to construct for them little tables and cupboards, and other utensils for holding their dolls and their trinkets. He had lived nearly six years in the same house with Miss Storey, and there is reason to believe that their youthful friendship gradually rose to a higher passion; but the smallness of her portion, and the inadequacy of his own fortune, appear to have prevented the consummation of their happiness. Miss Storey was afterwards twice married, and under the name of Mrs. Vincent, Dr. Stukeley visited her at Grantham in 1727, at the age of eighty-two, and obtained from her many particulars respecting the early history of our author. Newton's esteem for her continued unabated during his life. He regularly visited her when he went to Lincolnshire, and never failed to relieve her from little pecuniary difficulties which seem to have beset her family."

The schoolboy at Grantham was only fourteen years of age when his mother became a widow for the second time. She then returned to the old family home at Woolsthorpe, bringing with her the three children of her second marriage. Her means appear to have been somewhat scanty, and it was consequently thought necessary to recall Isaac from the school. His recently-born industry had been such that he had already made good progress in his studies, and his mother hoped that he would now lay aside his books, and those silent meditations to which, even at this early age, he had become addicted. It was expected that, instead of such pursuits, which were deemed quite useless, the boy would enter busily into the duties of the farm and the details of a country life. But before long it became manifest that the study of nature and the pursuit of knowledge had such a fascination for the youth that he could give little attention to aught else. It was plain that he would make but an indifferent farmer. He greatly preferred experimenting on his water-wheels to looking after labourers, while he found that working at mathematics behind a hedge was much more interesting than chaffering about the price of bullocks in the market place. Fortunately for humanity his mother, like a wise woman, determined to let her boy's genius have the scope which it required. He was accordingly sent back to Grantham school, with the object of being trained in the knowledge which would fit him for entering the University of Cambridge.

It was the 5th of June, 1660, when Isaac Newton, a youth of eighteen, was enrolled as an undergraduate of Trinity College, Cambridge. Little did those who sent him there dream that this boy was destined to be the most illustrious student who ever entered the portals of that great seat of learning. Little could the youth himself have foreseen that the rooms near the gateway which he occupied would acquire a celebrity from the fact that he dwelt in them, or that the ante-chapel of his college was in good time to be adorned by that noble statue, which is regarded as one of the chief art treasures of Cambridge University, both on account of its intrinsic beauty and the fact that it commemorates the fame of her most distinguished alumnus, Isaac Newton, the immortal astronomer. Indeed, his advent at the University seemed to have been by no means auspicious or brilliant. His birth was, as we have seen, comparatively obscure, and though he had already given indication of his capacity for reflecting on philosophical matters, yet he seems to have been but ill-equipped with the routine knowledge which youths are generally expected to take with them to the Universities.

From the outset of his college career, Newton's attention seems to have been mainly directed to mathematics. Here he began to give evidence of that marvellous insight into the deep secrets of nature which more than a century later led so dispassionate a judge as Laplace to pronounce Newton's immortal work as pre-eminent above all the productions of the human intellect. But though Newton was one of the very greatest mathematicians that ever lived, he was never a mathematician for the mere sake of mathematics. He employed his mathematics as an instrument for discovering the laws of nature. His industry and genius soon brought him under the notice of the University authorities. It is stated in the University records that he obtained a Scholarship in 1664. Two years later we find that Newton, as well as many residents in the

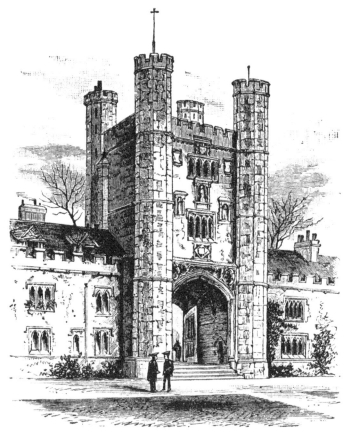

TRINITY COLLEGE, CAMBRIDGE.
Showing Newton's rooms; on the leads of the gateway he placed his telescope.

University, had to leave Cambridge temporarily on account of the breaking out of the plague. The philosopher retired for a season to his old home at Woolsthorpe, and there he remained until he was appointed a Fellow of Trinity College, Cambridge, in 1667. From this time onwards, Newton's reputation as a mathematician and as a natural philosopher steadily advanced, so that in 1669, while still but twenty-seven years of age, he was appointed to the distinguished position of Lucasian Professor of Mathematics at Cambridge. Here he found the opportunity to continue and develop that marvellous career of discovery which formed his life's work.

The earliest of Newton's great achievements in natural philosophy was his detection of the composite character of light. That a beam of ordinary sunlight is, in fact, a mixture of a very great number of different-coloured lights, is a doctrine now familiar to every one who has the slightest education in physical science. We must, however, remember that this discovery was really a tremendous advance in knowledge at the time when Newton announced it.

We here give the little diagram originally drawn by Newton, to explain the experiment by which he first learned the composition of light. A sunbeam is admitted into a darkened room through an open-

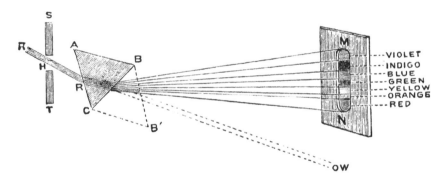

ing, H, in a shutter. This beam when not interfered with will travel in a straight line to the screen, and there reproduce a bright spot of the same shape as the hole in the shutter. If, however, a prism of glass, A B C, be introduced so that the beam traverse it, then it will be seen at once that the light is deflected from its original track. There is, however, a further and most important change which takes place. The spot of light is not alone removed to another part of the screen, but it becomes spread out into a long band beautifully coloured, and exhibiting the hues of the rainbow. At the top are the violet rays, and then in descending order we have the indigo, blue, green, yellow, orange, and red.

The circumstance in this phenomenon which appears to have particularly arrested Newton's attention, was the elongation which the luminous spot underwent in consequence of its passage through the prism. When the prism was absent the spot was nearly circular, but when the prism was introduced the spot was about five times as long as it was broad. To ascertain the explanation of this was the first problem to be solved. It seemed natural to suppose that it might be due to the thickness of the glass in the prism which the light traversed, or to the angle of incidence at which the light fell upon the prism. He found, however, upon careful trial, that the phenomenon could not be thus accounted for. It was not until after much patient labour that the true explanation dawned upon him. He discovered that though the beam of white light looks so pure and so simple, yet in reality it is composed of differently coloured lights blended together. These are, of course, indistinguishable in the compound beam, but they are separated or disentangled, so to speak, by the action of the prism. The rays at the blue end of the spectrum are more powerfully deflected by the action of the glass than are the rays at the red end. Thus, the rays variously coloured red, orange, yellow, green, blue, indigo, violet, are each conducted to a different part of the screen. In this way the prism has the effect of exhibiting the constitution of the composite beam of light.

To us this now seems quite obvious, but Newton did not adopt it hastily. With characteristic caution he verified the explanation by many different experiments, all of which confirmed his discovery. One of these may be mentioned. He made a hole in the screen at that part on which the violet rays fell. Thus a violet ray was allowed to pass through, all the rest of the light being intercepted, and on this beam so isolated he was able to try further experiments. For instance, when he interposed another prism in its path, he found, as he expected, that it was again deflected, and he measured the amount of the deflection. Again he tried the same experiment with one of the red rays from the opposite end of the coloured band. He allowed it to pass through the same aperture in the screen, and he tested the amount by which the second prism was capable of producing deflection. He thus found, as he had expected to find, that the second prism was more efficacious in bending the violet rays than in bending the red rays. Thus he confirmed the fact that the various hues of the rainbow were each bent by a prism to a different extent, violet being acted upon the most, and red the least.

Not only did Newton decompose a white beam into its constituent colours, but conversely by interposing a second prism with its angle turned upwards, he reunited the different colours, and thus reproduced the original beam of white light. In several other ways also he illustrated his famous proposition, which then seemed so startling, that white light was the result of a mixture of all hues of the rainbow. By combining painters' colours in the right proportion he did not in-

Isaac Newton

deed succeed in producing a mixture which would ordinarily be called white, but he obtained a grey pigment. Some of this he put on the floor of his room for comparison with a piece of white paper. He allowed a beam of bright sunlight to fall upon the paper and the mixed colours side by side, and a friend he called in for his opinion pronounced that under these circumstances the mixed colours looked the whiter of the two.

By repeated demonstrations Newton thus established his great discovery of the composite character of light. He at once perceived that his researches had an important bearing upon the principles involved in the construction of a telescope. Those who employed the telescope for looking at the stars, had been long aware of the imperfections which prevented all the various rays from being conducted to the same focus. But this imperfection had hitherto been erroneously accounted for. It had been supposed that the reason why success had not been attained in the construction of a refracting telescope was due to the fact that the object glass, made as it then was of a single piece, had not been properly shaped. Mathematicians had abundantly demonstrated that a single lens, if properly figured, must conduct all rays of light to the same focus, provided all rays experienced equal refraction in passing through the glass. Until Newton's discovery of the composition of white light, it had been taken for granted that the several rays in a white beam were equally refrangible. No doubt if this had been the case, a perfect telescope could have been produced by properly shaping the object glass. But when Newton had demonstrated that light was by no means so simple as had been supposed, it became obvious that a satisfactory refracting telescope was an impossibility when only a single object lens was employed, however carefully that lens might have been wrought. Such an objective might, no doubt, be made to conduct any one group of rays of a particular shade to the same focus, but the rays of other colours in the beam of white light must necessarily travel somewhat astray. In this way Newton accounted for a great part of the difficulties which had hitherto beset the attempts to construct a perfect refracting telescope.

We now know how these difficulties can be, to a great extent, overcome, by employing for the objective a composite lens made of two pieces of glass possessing different qualities. To these achromatic object glasses, as they are called, the great development of astronomical knowledge, since Newton's time, is due. But it must be remarked that, although the theoretical possibility of constructing an achromatic lens was investigated by Newton, he certainly came to the conclusion that the difficulty could not be removed by employing a composite objective, with two different kinds of glass. In this his marvellous sagacity in the interpretation of nature seems for once to have deserted him. We can, however, hardly regret that Newton failed to discover the achromatic objective, when we observe that it was in consequence of his deeming an achromatic objective to be impossible that he was led to the invention of the reflecting telescope. Finding, as he believed, that the defects of the telescope could not be remedied by any application of the principle of refraction he was led to look in quite a different direction for the improvement of the tool on which the advancement of astronomy depended. The *refraction* of light depended as he had found, upon the colour of the light. The laws of *reflection* were, however, quite independent of the colour. Whether rays be red or green, blue or yellow, they are all reflected in precisely the same manner from a mirror. Accordingly, Newton perceived that if he could construct a telescope the action of which depended upon reflection, instead of upon refraction, the difficulty which had hitherto proved an insuperable obstacle to the improvement of the instrument would be evaded.

For this purpose Newton fashioned a concave mirror from a mixture of copper and tin, a combination which gives a surface with al-

SIR ISAAC NEWTON'S LITTLE REFLECTOR.

most the lustre of silver. When the light of a star fell upon the surface, an image of the star was produced in the focus of this mirror, and then this image was examined by a magnifying eye-piece. Such is the principle of the famous reflecting telescope which bears the name of Newton. The little reflector which he constructed, represented in the adjoining figure, is still preserved as one of the treasures of the Royal Society. The telescope tube had the very modest dimension of one inch in diameter. It was, however, the precursor of a whole series of magnificent instruments, each outstripping the other in magnitude, until at last the culminating point was attained in 1845, by the construction of Lord Rosse's mammoth reflector of six feet in aperture.

Newton's discovery of the composition of light led to an embittered controversy, which caused no little worry to the great Philosopher. Some of those who attacked him enjoyed considerable and, it must be admitted, even well-merited repute in the ranks of science. They alleged, however, that the elongation of the coloured band which Newton had noticed was due to this, to that, or to the other—to anything, in fact, rather than to the true cause which Newton assigned. With characteristic patience and love of truth, Newton steadily replied to each such attack. He showed most completely how utterly his adversaries had misunderstood the subject, and how slight indeed was their acquaintance with the natural phenomenon in question. In reply to each point raised, he was ever able to cite fresh experiments and adduce fresh illustrations, until at last his opponents retired worsted from the combat.

It has been often a matter for surprise that Newton, throughout his whole career, should have taken so much trouble to expose the errors of those who attacked his views. He used even to do this when it plainly appeared that his adversaries did not understand the subject they were discussing. A philosopher might have said, "I know I am right, and whether others think I am right or not may be a matter of concern to them, but it is certainly not a matter about which I need trouble. If after having been told the truth they elect to remain in error, so much the worse for them; my time can be better employed than in seeking to put such people right." This, however, was not Newton's method. He spent much valuable time in overthrowing objections which were often of a very futile description. Indeed, he suffered a great deal of annoyance from the persistency, and in some cases one might almost say from the rancour, of the attacks which were made upon him. Unfortunately for himself, he did not possess that capacity for sublime indifference to what men may say, which is often the happy possession of intellects greatly inferior to his.

The subject of optics still continuing to engross Newton's attention, he followed up his researches into the structure of the sunbeam by many other valuable investigations in connection with light. Every one has noticed the beautiful colours manifested in a soap-bubble. Here was a subject which not unnaturally attracted the attention of one who had expounded the colours of the spectrum with such success. He perceived that similar hues were produced by other thin plates of transparent material besides soap-bubbles, and his ingenuity was sufficient to devise a method by which the thicknesses of the different films could be measured. We can hardly, indeed, say that a like success attended his interpretation of these phenomena to that which had been so conspicuous in his explanation of the spectrum. It implies no disparagement to the sublime genius of Newton to admit that the doctrines he put forth as to the causes of the colours in the soap-bubbles can be no longer accepted. We must remember that Newton was a pioneer in accounting for the physical properties of light. The facts that he established are indeed unquestionable, but the explanations which he was led to offer of some of them are seen to be untenable in the fuller light of our present knowledge.

Had Newton done nothing beyond making his wonderful discoveries in light, his fame would have gone down to posterity as one of the greatest of Nature's interpreters. But it was reserved for him to accomplish other discoveries, which have pushed even his analysis of the sunbeam into the background; it is he who has expounded the system of the universe by the discovery of the law of universal gravitation.

The age had indeed become ripe for the advent of the genius of Newton. Kepler had discovered with marvellous penetration the laws which govern the movements of the planets around the sun, and in various directions it had been more or less vaguely felt that the explanation of Kepler's laws, as well as of many other phenomena, must be sought for in connection with the attractive power of matter. But the

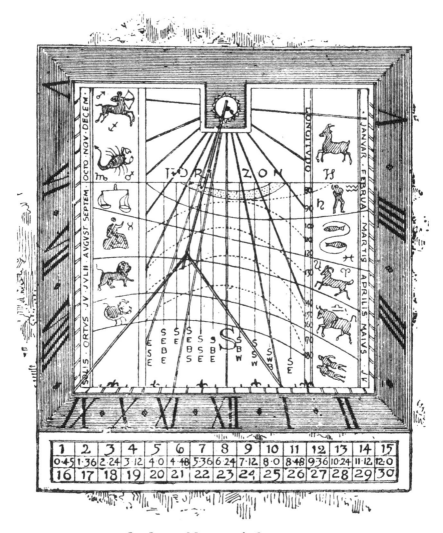

SIR ISAAC NEWTON'S SUN-DIAL.

mathematical analysis which alone could deal with this subject was wanting; it had to be created by Newton.

At Woolsthorpe, in the year 1666, Newton's attention appears to have been concentrated upon the subject of gravitation. Whatever may be the extent to which we accept the more or less mythical story as to how the fall of an apple first directed the attention of the philosopher to the fact that gravitation must extend through space, it seems, at all events, certain that this is an excellent illustration of the line of reasoning which he followed. He argued in this way. The earth attracts the apple; it would do so, no matter how high might be the tree from which that apple fell. It would then seem to follow that this power which resides in the earth by which it can draw all external bodies towards it, extends far beyond the altitude of the loftiest tree. Indeed, we seem to find no limit to it. At the greatest elevation that has ever been attained, the attractive power of the earth is still exerted, and though we cannot by any actual experiment reach an altitude more than a few miles above the earth, yet it is certain that gravitation would extend to elevations far greater. It is plain, thought Newton, that an apple let fall from a point a hundred miles above this earth's surface, would be drawn down by the attraction, and would continually gather fresh velocity until it reached the ground. From a hundred miles it was natural to think of what would happen at a thousand miles, or at hundreds of thousands of miles. No doubt the intensity of the attraction becomes weaker with every increase in the altitude, but that action would still exist to some extent, however lofty might be the elevation which had been attained.

It then occurred to Newton, that though the moon is at a distance of two hundred and forty thousand miles from the earth, yet the attractive power of the earth must extend to the moon. He was particularly led to think of the moon in this connection, not only because the moon is so much closer to the earth than are any other celestial bodies, but also because the moon is an appendage to the earth, always revolving around it. The moon is certainly attracted to the earth, and yet the moon does not fall down; how is this to be accounted for? The explanation was to be found in the character of the moon's present motion. If the moon were left for a moment at rest, there can be no doubt that the attraction of the earth would begin to draw the lunar globe in towards our globe. In the course of a few days our satellite would come down on the earth with a most fearful crash. This catastrophe is averted by the circumstance that the moon has a movement of revolution around the earth. Newton was able to calculate from the known laws of mechanics, which he had himself been mainly instrumental in discovering, what the attractive power of the earth must be, so that the moon shall move precisely as we find it to move. It then appeared that the very power which makes an apple fall at the earth's surface is the power which guides the moon in its orbit.

Once this step had been taken, the whole scheme of the universe might almost be said to have become unrolled before the eye of the philosopher. It was natural to suppose that just as the moon was guided and controlled by the attraction of the earth, so the earth itself, in the course of its great annual progress, should be guided and controlled by the supreme attractive power of the sun. If this were so with regard to the earth, then it would be impossible to doubt that in the same way the movements of the planets could be explained to be consequences of solar attraction.

Sir Isaac Newton's Telescope.

It was at this point that the great laws of Kepler became especially significant. Kepler had shown how each of the planets revolves in an ellipse around the sun, which is situated on one of the foci. This discovery had been arrived at from the interpretation of observations. Kepler had himself assigned no reason why the orbit of a planet should be an ellipse rather than any other of the infinite number of closed curves which might be traced around the sun. Kepler had also shown, and here again he was merely deducing the results from observation, that when the movements of two planets were compared together, the squares of the periodic times in which each planet revolved were proportional to the cubes of their mean distances from the sun. This also

Kepler merely knew to be true as a fact, he gave no demonstration of the reason why nature should have adopted this particular relation between the distance and the periodic time rather than any other. Then, too, there was the law by which Kepler with unparalleled ingenuity, explained the way in which the velocity of a planet varies at the different points of its track, when he showed how the line drawn from the sun to the planet described equal areas around the sun in equal times. These were the materials with which Newton set to work. He proposed to infer from these the actual laws regulating the force by which the sun guides the planets. Here it was that his sublime mathematical genius came into play. Step by step Newton advanced until he had completely accounted for all the phenomena.

In the first place, he showed that as the planet describes equal areas in equal times about the sun, the attractive force which the sun exerts upon it must necessarily be directed in a straight line towards the sun itself. He also demonstrated the converse truth, that whatever be the nature of the force which emanated from a sun, yet so long as that force was directed through the sun's centre, any body which revolved around it must describe equal areas in equal times, and this it must do, whatever be the actual character of the law according to which the intensity of the force varies at different parts of the planet's journey. Thus the first advance was taken in the exposition of the scheme of the universe.

The next step was to determine the law according to which the force thus proved to reside in the sun varied with the distance of the planet. Newton presently showed by a most superb effort of mathematical reasoning, that if the orbit of a planet were an ellipse and if the sun were at one of the foci of that ellipse, the intensity of the attractive force must vary inversely as the square of the planet's distance. If the law had any other expression than the inverse square of the distance, then the orbit which the planet must follow would not be an ellipse; or if an ellipse, it would, at all events, not have the sun in the focus. Hence he was able to show from Kepler's laws alone that the force which guided the planets was an attractive power emanating from the sun, and that the intensity of this attractive power varied with the inverse square of the distance between the two bodies.

These circumstances being known, it was then easy to show that the

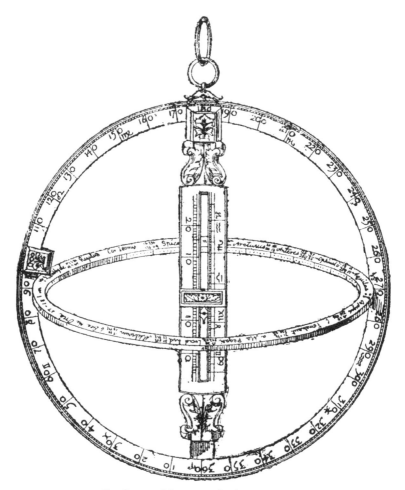

SIR ISAAC NEWTON'S ASTROLABE.

last of Kepler's three laws must necessarily follow. If a number of planets were revolving around the sun, then supposing the materials of all these bodies were equally affected by gravitation, it can be demonstrated that the square of the periodic time in which each planet completes its orbit is proportional to the cube of the greatest diameter in that orbit.

These superb discoveries were, however, but the starting point from which Newton entered on a series of researches, which disclosed many of the profoundest secrets in the scheme of celestial mechanics. His natural insight showed that not only large masses like the sun and the earth, and the moon, attract each other, but that every particle in the universe must attract every other particle with a force which varies inversely as the square of the distance between them. If, for example, the two particles were placed twice as far apart, then the intensity of the force which sought to bring them together would be reduced to one-fourth. If two particles, originally ten miles asunder, attracted each other with a certain force, then, when the distance was reduced to one mile, the intensity of the attraction between the two particles would be increased one-hundred-fold. This fertile principle extends throughout the whole of nature. In some cases, however, the calculation of its effect upon the actual problems of nature would be hardly possible, were it not for another discovery which Newton's genius enabled him to accomplish. In the case of two globes like the earth and the moon, we must remember that we are dealing not with particles, but with two mighty masses of matter, each composed of innumerable myriads of particles. Every particle in the earth does attract every particle in the moon with a force which varies inversely as the square of their distance. The calculation of such attractions is rendered feasible by the following principle. Assuming that the earth consists of materials symmetrically arranged in shells of varying densities, we may then, in calculating its attraction, regard the whole mass of the globe as concentrated at its centre. Similarly we may regard the moon as concentrated at the centre of its mass. In this way the earth and the moon can both be regarded as particles in point of size, each particle having, however, the entire mass of the corresponding globe. The attraction of one particle for another is a much more simple matter to investigate than the attraction of the myriad different points of the earth upon the myriad different points of the moon.

Many great discoveries now crowded in upon Newton. He first of all gave the explanation of the tides that ebb and flow around our shores. Even in the earliest times the tides had been shown to be related to the moon. It was noticed that the tides were specially high during full moon or during new moon, and this circumstance obviously pointed to the existence of some connection between the moon and these movements of the water, though as to what that connection was no one had any accurate conception until Newton announced the law of gravitation. Newton then made it plain that the rise and fall of the water was simply a consequence of the attractive power which the moon exerted upon the oceans lying upon our globe. He showed also that to a certain extent the sun produces tides, and he was able to explain how it was that when the sun and the moon both conspire, the joint result was to produce especially high tides, which we call "spring tides"; whereas if the solar tide was low, while the lunar tide was high, then we had the phenomenon of "neap" tides.

But perhaps the most signal of Newton's applications of the law of gravitation was connected with certain irregularities in the movements of the moon. In its orbit round the earth our satellite is, of course, mainly guided by the great attraction of our globe. If there were no other body in the universe, then the centre of the moon must necessarily perform an ellipse, and the centre of the earth would lie in the focus of that ellipse. Nature, however, does not allow the movements to possess the simplicity which this arrangement would imply, for the sun is present as a source of disturbance. The sun attracts the moon, and the sun attracts the earth, but in different degrees, and the consequence is that the moon's movement with regard to the earth is seriously affected by the influence of the sun. It is not allowed to move exactly in an ellipse, nor is the earth exactly in the focus. How great was Newton's achievement in the solution of this problem will be appreciated if we realise that he not only had to determine from the law of gravitation the nature of the disturbance of the moon, but he had actually to construct the mathematical tools by which alone such calculations could be effected.

The resources of Newton's genius seemed, however, to prove equal to almost any demand that could be made upon it. He saw that each planet must disturb the other, and in that way he was able to render a satisfactory account of certain phenomena which had perplexed all preceding investigators. That mysterious movement by which the pole of the earth sways about among the stars had been long an unsolved enigma, but Newton showed that the moon grasped with its attraction the protuberant mass at the equatorial regions of the earth, and thus tilted the earth's axis in a way that accounted for the phenomenon which had been known but had never been explained for two thousand years. All these discoveries were brought together in that immortal work, Newton's "Principia."

Down to the year 1687, when the "Principia" was published, Newton had lived the life of a recluse at Cambridge, being entirely occupied with those transcendent researches to which we have referred. But in that year he issued from his seclusion under circumstances of considerable historical interest. King James the Second attempted an invasion of the rights and privileges of the University of Cambridge by issuing a command that Father Francis, a Benedictine monk, should be received as a Master of Arts in the University, without having taken the oaths of allegiance and supremacy. With this arbitrary command the University sternly refused to comply. The Vice-Chancellor was accordingly summoned to answer for an act of contempt to the authority of the Crown. Newton was one of nine delegates who were chosen to defend the independence of the University before the High Court. They were able to show that Charles the Second, who had issued a *mandamus* under somewhat similar circumstances, had been induced after due consideration to withdraw it. This argument appeared satisfactory, and the University gained their case. Newton's next step in public life was his election, by a narrow majority, as member for the University, and during the years 1688 and 1689, he seems to have attended to his parliamentary duties with considerable regularity.

An incident which happened in 1692 was apparently the cause of considerable disturbance in Newton's equanimity, if not in his health. He had gone to early morning chapel, leaving a lighted candle among his papers on his desk. Tradition asserts that his little dog "Diamond" upset the candle; at all events, when Newton came back he found that many valuable papers had perished in a conflagration. The loss of these manuscripts seems to have had a serious effect. Indeed, it has been asserted that the distress reduced Newton to a state of mental aberration for a considerable time. This has, apparently, not been confirmed, but there is no doubt that he experienced considerable disquiet, for in writing on September 13th, 1693, to Mr. Pepys, he says:

"I am extremely troubled at the embroilment I am in, and have neither ate nor slept well this twelve-month, nor have my former consistency of mind."

Notwithstanding the fame which Newton had achieved, by the publication of his, "Principia," and by all his researches, the State had not as yet taken any notice whatever of the most illustrious man of science that this or any other country has ever produced. Many of his friends had exerted themselves to procure him some permanent appointment, but without success. It happened, however, that Mr. Montagu, who had sat with Newton in Parliament, was appointed Chancellor of the Exchequer in 1694. Ambitious of distinction in his new office, Mr. Montagu addressed himself to the improvement of the current coin, which was then in a very debased condition. It fortunately happened that an opportunity occurred of appointing a new official in the Mint; and Mr. Montagu on the 19th of March, 1695, wrote to offer Mr. Newton the position of warden. The salary was to be five or six hundred a year, and the business would not require more attendance than Newton could spare. The Lucasian professor accepted this post, and forthwith entered upon his new duties.

The knowledge of physics which Newton had acquired by his experiments was of much use in connection with his duties at the Mint. He carried out the re-coinage with great skill in the course of two years, and as a reward for his exertions, he was appointed, in 1697, to the Mastership of the Mint, with a salary between 1,200 Pounds and 1,500 Pounds per annum. In 1701, his duties at the Mint being so engrossing, he resigned his Lucasian professorship at Cambridge, and at the same time he had to surrender his fellowship at Trinity College. This closed his connection with the University of Cambridge. It should, however, be remarked that at a somewhat earlier stage in his career he was very nearly being appointed to an office which might have enabled the University to retain the great philosopher within its precincts. Some of his friends had almost succeeded in securing his nomination to the Provostship of King's College, Cambridge; the appointment, however, fell through, inasmuch as the statute could not be evaded, which required that the Provost of King's College should be in holy orders.

In those days it was often the custom for illustrious mathematicians, when they had discovered a solution for some new and striking problem, to publish that problem as a challenge to the world, while withholding their own solution. A famous instance of this is found in what is known as the Brachistochrone problem, which was solved by John Bernouilli. The nature of this problem may be mentioned. It was to find the shape of the curve along which a body would slide down from one point (A) to another point (B) in the shortest time. It might at first be thought that the straight line from A to B, as it is undoubtedly the shortest distance between the points, would also be the path of quickest descent; but this is not so. There is a curved line, down which a bead, let us say, would run on a smooth wire from A to B in a shorter time than the same bead would require to run down the straight wire. Bernouilli's problem was to find out what that curve must be. Newton solved it correctly; he showed that the curve was a part of what is termed a cycloid—that is to say, a curve like that which is described by a point on the rim of a carriage-wheel as the wheel runs along the ground. Such was Newton's geometrical insight that he was able to transmit a solution of the problem on the day after he had received it, to the President of the Royal Society.

In 1703 Newton, whose world wide fame was now established, was elected President of the Royal Society. Year after year he was re-elected to this distinguished position, and his tenure, which lasted twenty-five years, only terminated with his life. It was in discharge of his duties as President of the Royal Society that Newton was brought into contact with Prince George of Denmark. In April, 1705, the Queen paid a visit to Cambridge as the guest of Dr. Bentley, the then Master of Trinity, and in a court held at Trinity Lodge on April 15th, 1705, the honour of knighthood was conferred upon the discoverer of gravitation.

Urged by illustrious friends, who sought the promotion of knowledge, Newton gave his attention to the publication of a new edition of the "Principia." His duties at the Mint, however, added to the supreme duty of carrying on his original investigations, left him but little time for the more ordinary task of the revision. He was accordingly induced to associate with himself for this purpose a distinguished young mathematician, Roger Coates, a Fellow of Trinity College, Cambridge, who had recently been appointed Plumian Professor of Astronomy. On July 27th, 1713, Newton, by this time a favourite at Court, waited on the Queen, and presented her with a copy of the new edition of the "Principia."

Throughout his life Newton appears to have been greatly interested in theological studies, and he specially devoted his attention to the subject of prophecy. He left behind him a manuscript on the prophecies of Daniel and the Apocalypse of St. John, and he also wrote various theological papers. Many other subjects had from time to time engaged his attention. He studied the laws of heat; he experimented in pursuit of the dreams of the Alchymist; while the philosopher who had revealed the mechanism of the heavens found occasional relaxation in trying to interpret hieroglyphics. In the last few years of his life he bore with fortitude a painful ailment, and on Monday, March 20th, 1727, he died in the eighty-fifth year of his age. On Tuesday, March 28th, he was buried in Westminster Abbey.

Though Newton lived long enough to receive the honour that his astonishing discoveries so justly merited, and though for many years of his life his renown was much greater than that of any of his contemporaries, yet it is not too much to say that, in the years which have since elapsed, Newton's fame has been ever steadily advancing, so that it never stood higher than it does at this moment.

We hardly know whether to admire more the sublime discoveries at which he arrived, or the extraordinary character of the intellectual processes by which those discoveries were reached. Viewed from either standpoint, Newton's "Principia" is incomparably the greatest work on science that has ever yet been produced.

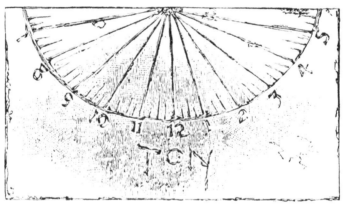

SIR ISAAC NEWTON'S SUN-DIAL IN THE ROYAL SOCIETY.

FLAMSTEED.

Among the manuscripts preserved at Greenwich Observatory are certain documents in which Flamsteed gives an account of his own life. We may commence our sketch by quoting the following passage from this autobiography:—"To keep myself from idleness, and to recreate myself, I have intended here to give some account of my life, in my youth, before the actions thereof, and the providences of God therein, be too far passed out of my memory; and to observe the accidents of all my years, and inclinations of my mind, that whosoever may light upon these papers may see I was not so wholly taken up, either with my father's business or my mathematics, but that I both admitted and found time for other as weighty considerations."

The chief interest which attaches to the name of Flamsteed arises from the fact that he was the first of the illustrious series of Astronomers Royal who have presided over Greenwich Observatory. In that capacity Flamsteed was able to render material assistance to Newton by providing him with the observations which his lunar theory required.

John Flamsteed was born at Denby, in Derbyshire, on the 19th of August, 1646. His mother died when he was three years old, and the second wife, whom his father took three years later, only lived until Flamsteed was eight, there being also two younger sisters. In his boyhood the future astronomer tells us that he was very fond of those romances which affect boy's imagination, but as he writes, "At twelve years of age I left all the wild ones and betook myself to read the better sort of them, which, though they were not probable, yet carried no seeming impossibility in the picturing." By the time Flamsteed was fifteen years old he had embarked in still more serious work, for he had read Plutarch's "Lives," Tacitus' "Roman History," and many other books of a similar description. In 1661 he became ill with some serious rheumatic affection, which obliged him to be withdrawn from school. It was then for the first time that he received the rudiments of a scientific education. He had, however, attained his sixteenth year before he made any progress in arithmetic. He tells us how his father taught him "the doctrine of fractions," and "the golden rule of three"—lessons which he seemed to have learned easily and quickly. One of the books which he read at this time directed his attention to astronomical instruments, and he was thus led to construct for himself a quadrant, by which he could take some simple astronomical observations. He further calculated a table to give the sun's altitudes at different hours, and thus displayed those tastes for practical astronomy which he lived to develop so greatly. It appears that these scientific studies were discountenanced by his father, who designed that his son should follow a business career. Flamsteed's natural inclination, however, forced him to prosecute astronomical work, notwithstanding the impediments that lay in his path. Unfortunately, his constitutional delicacy seems to have increased, and he had just completed his eighteenth year, "when," to use his own words, "the winter came on and thrust me again into the chimney, whence the heat and the dryness of the preceding summer had happily once before withdrawn me. But, it not being a fit season for physic, it was thought fit to let me alone this winter, and try the skill of another physician on me in the spring."

It appears that at this time a quack named Valentine Greatrackes, was reputed to have effected most astonishing cures in Ireland merely by the stroke of his hands, without the application of any medicine whatever. Flamsteed's father, despairing of any remedy for his son from the legitimate branch of the profession, despatched him to Ireland on August 26th, 1665, he being then, as recorded with astronomical accuracy, "nineteen years, six days, and eleven hours old." The young astronomer, accompanied by a friend, arrived on a Tuesday at Liverpool but the wind not being favourable, they remained there till the following Friday, when a shift of the wind to the east took place. They embarked accordingly on a vessel called the SUPPLY at noon, and on Saturday night came in sight of Dublin. Ere they could land, however, they were nearly being wrecked on Lambay Island. This peril safely passed, there was a long delay for quarantine before they were at last allowed on shore. On Thursday, September 6th, they set out from Dublin, where they had been sojourning at the "Ship" Hotel, in Dame Street, towards Assaune, where Greatrackes received his patients.

Flamsteed gives an interesting account of his travels in Ireland. They dined at Naas on the first day, and on September 8th they reached Carlow, a town which is described as one of the fairest they

FLAMSTEED'S HOUSE.

saw on their journey. By Sunday morning, September 10th, having lost their way several times, they reached Castleton, called commonly Four Mile Waters. Flamsteed inquired of the host in the inn where they might find a church, but was told that the minister lived twelve miles away, and that they had no sermon except when he came to receive his tithes once a year, and a woman added that "they had plenty enough of everything necessary except the word of God." The travellers accordingly went on to Cappoquin, which lies up the river Blackwater, on the road to Lismore, eight miles from Youghal. Thence they immediately started on foot to Assaune. About a mile from Cappoquin, and entering into the house of Mr. Greatrackes, they saw him touch several patients, "whereof some were nearly cured, others were on the mending hand, and some on whom his strokes had no effect." Flamsteed was touched by the famous quack on the afternoon of September 11th, but we are hardly surprised to hear his remark that "he found not his disease to stir." Next morning the astronomer came again to see Mr. Greatrackes, who had "a kind of majestical yet affable presence, and a composed carriage." Even after the third touching had been submitted to, no benefit seems to have been derived. We must, however record, to the credit of Mr. Greatrackes, that he refused to accept any payment from Flamsteed, because he was a stranger.

Finding it useless to protract his stay any longer, Flamsteed and his friend set out on their return to Dublin. In the course of his journey he seems to have been much impressed with Clonmel, which he describes as an "exceedingly pleasantly seated town." But in those days a journey to Ireland was so serious an enterprise that when Flamsteed did arrive safely back at Derby after an absence of a month, he adds, "For God's providence in this journey, His name be praised, Amen."

As to the expected benefits to his health from the expedition we may quote his own words: "In the winter following I was indifferent hearty, and my disease was not so violent as it used to be at that time formerly. But whether through God's mercy I received this through Mr. Greatrackes' touch, or my journey and vomiting at sea, I am uncertain; but, by some circumstances, I guess that I received a benefit from both."

It is evident that by this time Flamsteed's interest in all astronomical matters had greatly increased. He studied the construction of sundials, he formed a catalogue of seventy of the fixed stars, with their places on the heavens, and he computed the circumstances of the solar eclipse which was to happen on June 22nd, 1666. It is interesting to note that even in those days the doctrines of the astrologers still found a considerable degree of credence, and Flamsteed spent a good deal of his time in astrological studies and computations. He investigated the methods of casting a nativity, but a suspicion, or, indeed, rather more than a suspicion, seems to have crossed his mind as to the value of these astrological predictions, for he says in fine, "I found astrology to give generally strong conjectural hints, not perfect declarations."

All this time, however, the future Astronomer Royal was steadily advancing in astronomical inquiries of a recondite nature. He had investigated the obliquity of the ecliptic with extreme care, so far as the circumstances of astronomical observation would at that time permit. He had also sought to discover the sun's distance from the earth in so far as it could be obtained by determining when the moon was exactly half illuminated, and he had measured, with much accuracy, the length of the tropical year. It will thus be seen that, even at the age of twenty, Flamsteed had made marked progress, considering how much his time had been interfered with by ill-health.

Other branches of astronomy began also to claim his attention. We learn that in 1669 and 1670 he compared the planets Jupiter and Mars with certain fixed stars near which they passed. His instrumental means, though very imperfect, were still sufficient to enable him to measure the intervals on the celestial sphere between the planets and the stars. As the places of the stars were known, Flamsteed was thus able to obtain the places of the planets. This is substantially the way in which astronomers of the present day still proceed when they desire to determine the places of the planets, inasmuch as, directly or indirectly those places are always obtained relatively to the fixed stars. By his observations at this early period, Flamsteed was, it is true, not able to obtain any great degree of accuracy; he succeeded, however, in proving that the tables by which the places of the planets were ordinarily given were not to be relied upon.

Flamsteed's labours in astronomy and in the allied branches of science were now becoming generally known, and he gradually came to correspond with many distinguished men of learning. One of the first occasions which brought the talents of the young astronomer into fame was the publication of some calculations concerning certain astronomical phenomena which were to happen in the year 1670. In the monthly revolution of the moon its disc passes over those stars which lie along its track. The disappearance of a star by the interposition of the moon is called an "occultation." Owing to the fact that our satellite is comparatively near us, the position which the moon appears to oc-

Flamsteed.

cupy on the heavens varies from different parts of the earth, it consequently happens that a star which would be occulted to an observer in
one locality, would often not be occulted to an observer who was situated elsewhere. Even when an occultation is visible from both places,
the times at which the star disappears from view will, generally speaking, be different. Much calculation is therefore necessary to decide the
circumstances under which the occultations of stars may be visible

from any particular station. Having a taste for such computations, Flamsteed calculated the occultations which were to happen in the year 1670, it being the case that several remarkable stars would be passed over by the moon during this year. Of course at the present time, we find such information duly set forth in the *Nautical Almanac*, but a couple of centuries ago there was no such source of astronomical knowledge as is now to be found in that invaluable publication, which astronomers and navigators know so well. Flamsteed accordingly sent the results of his work to the President of the Royal Society. The paper which contained them was received very favourably, and at once brought Flamsteed into notice among the most eminent members of that illustrious body, one of whom, Mr. Collins, became through life his faithful friend and constant correspondent. Flamsteed's father was naturally gratified with the remarkable notice which his son was receiving from the great and learned; accordingly he desired him to go to London, that he might make the personal acquaintance of those scientific friends whom he had only known by correspondence previously. Flamsteed was indeed glad to avail himself of this opportunity. Thus he became acquainted with Dr. Barrow, and especially with Newton, who was then Lucasian Professor of Mathematics at Cambridge. It seems to have been in consequence of this visit to London that Flamsteed entered himself as a member of Jesus College, Cambridge. We have but little information as to his University career, but at all events he took his degree of M.A. on June 5th, 1674.

Up to this time it would seem that Flamsteed had been engaged, to a certain extent, in the business carried on by his father. It is true that he does not give any explicit details, yet there are frequent references to journeys which he had to take on business matters. But the time now approached when Flamsteed was to start on an independent career, and it appears that he took his degree in Cambridge with the object of entering into holy orders, so that he might settle in a small living near Derby, which was in the gift of a friend of his father, and would be at the disposal of the young astronomer. This scheme was, however, not carried out, but Flamsteed does not tell us why it failed, his only remark being, that "the good providence of God that had designed me for another station ordered it otherwise."

Sir Jonas Moore, one of the influential friends whom Flamsteed's talents had attracted, seems to have procured for him the position of king's astronomer, with a salary of 100 pounds per annum. A larger salary appears to have been designed at first for this office, which was now being newly created, but as Flamsteed was resolved on taking holy orders, a lesser salary was in his case deemed sufficient. The building of the observatory, in which the first Astronomer Royal was to be installed, seems to have been brought about, or, at all events, its progress was accelerated, in a somewhat curious manner.

A Frenchman, named Le Sieur de S. Pierre, came over to London to promulgate a scheme for discovering longitudes, then a question of much importance. He brought with him introductions to distinguished people, and his mission attracted a great deal of attention. The proposals which he made came under Flamsteed's notice, who pointed out that the Frenchman's projects were quite inapplicable in the present state of astronomical science, inasmuch as the places of the stars were not known with the degree of accuracy which would be necessary if such methods were to be rendered available. Flamsteed then goes on to say:—"I heard no more of the Frenchman after this; but was told that my letters had been shown King Charles. He was startled at the assertion of the fixed stars' places being false in the catalogue, and said, with some vehemence, he must have them anew observed, examined, and corrected, for the use of his seamen."

The first question to be settled was the site for the new observatory. Hyde Park and Chelsea College were both mentioned as suitable localities, but, at Sir Christopher Wren's suggestion, Greenwich Hill was finally resolved upon. The king made a grant of five hundred pounds of money. He gave bricks from Tilbury Fort, while materials, in the shape of wood, iron, and lead, were available from a gatehouse demolished in the Tower. The king also promised whatever further material aid might be shown to be necessary. The first stone of the Royal Observatory was laid on August 10th, 1675, and within a few years a building was erected in which the art of modern practical astronomy was to be created. Flamsteed strove with extraordinary diligence, and in spite of many difficulties, to obtain a due provision of astronomical instruments, and to arrange for the carrying on of his observations. Notwithstanding the king's promises, the astronomer was, however, but scant-ily provided with means, and he had no assistants to help him in his work. It follows that all the observations, as well as the reductions, and, indeed, all the incidental work of the observatory, had to be carried on by himself alone. Flamsteed, as we have seen, had, however, many staunch friends. Sir Jonas Moore in particular at all times rendered him most valuable assistance, and encouraged him by the warm sympathy and keen interest which he showed in astronomy. The work of the first Astronomer Royal was frequently interrupted by recurrent attacks of the complaints to which we have already referred. He says himself that "his distempers stick so close that that he cannot remove them," and he lost much time by prostration from headaches, as well as from more serious affections.

The year 1678 found him in the full tide of work in his observatory. He was specially engaged on the problem of the earth's motion, which he sought to derive from observations of the sun and of Venus. But this, as well as many other astronomical researches which he under-took, were only subsidiary to that which he made the main task of his life, namely, the formation of a catalogue of fixed stars. At the time when Flamsteed commenced his career, the only available catalogue of fixed stars was that of Tycho Brahe. This work had been published at the commencement of the seventeenth century, and it contained about a thousand stars. The positions assigned to these stars, though obtained with wonderful skill, considering the many difficulties under which Tycho laboured, were quite inaccurate when judged by our modern standards. Tycho's instruments were necessarily most rudely divided, and he had, of course, no telescopes to aid him. Consequently it was merely by a process of sighting that he could obtain the places of the stars. It must further be remembered that Tycho had no clocks, and no micrometers. He had, indeed, but little correct knowledge of the motions of the heavenly bodies to guide him. To determine the longitudes of a few principal stars he conceived the ingenious idea of measuring by day the position of Venus with respect to the sun, an ob-servation which the exceptional brightness of this planet rendered pos-sible without telescopic aid, and then by night he observed the position of Venus with regard to the stars.

It has been well remarked by Mr. Baily, in his introduction to the "British Catalogue of Stars," that "Flamsteed's observations, by a fortunate combination of circumstances, commenced a new and a brilliant era. It happened that, at that period, the powerful mind of Newton was directed to this subject; a friendly intercourse then existed between these two distinguished characters; and thus the first observations that could lay any claim to accuracy were at once brought in aid of those deep researches in which our illustrious geometer was then engaged. The first edition of the 'Principia' bears testimony to the assistance afforded by Flamsteed to Newton in these inquiries; although the former considers that the acknowledgment is not so ample as it ought to have been."

Although Flamsteed's observations can hardly be said to possess the accuracy of those made in more recent times, when instruments so much superior to his have been available, yet they possess an interest of a special kind from their very antiquity. This circumstance renders them of particular importance to the astronomer, inasmuch as they are calculated to throw light on the proper motions of the stars. Flamsteed's work may, indeed, be regarded as the origin of all subsequent catalogues, and the nomenclature which he adopted, though in some respects it can hardly be said to be very defensible, is, nevertheless, that which has been adopted by all subsequent astronomers. There were also a great many errors, as might be expected in a work of such extent, composed almost entirely of numerical detail. Many of these errors have been corrected by Baily himself, the assiduous editor of "Flamsteed's Life and Works," for Flamsteed was so harassed from various causes in the latter part of his life, and was so subject to infirmities all through his career, that he was unable to revise his computations with the care that would have been necessary. Indeed, he observed many additional stars which he never included in the British Catalogue. It is, as Baily well remarks, "rather a matter of astonishment that he accomplished so much, considering his slender means, his weak frame, and the vexations which he constantly experienced."

Flamsteed had the misfortune, in the latter part of his life, to become estranged from his most eminent scientific contemporaries. He had supplied Newton with places of the moon, at the urgent solicitation of the author of the "Principia," in order that the lunar theory should be carefully compared with observation. But Flamsteed appears to have thought that in Newton's further request for similar information, he appeared to be demanding as a right that which Flamsteed considered he was only called upon to render as a favour. A considerable dispute grew out of this matter, and there are many letters and documents, bearing on the difficulties which subsequently arose, that are not, perhaps, very creditable to either party.

Notwithstanding his feeble constitution, Flamsteed lived to the age of seventy-three, his death occurring on the last day of the year 1719.

HALLEY.

Isaac Newton was just fourteen years of age when the birth of Edmund Halley, who was destined in after years to become Newton's warmly attached friend, and one of his most illustrious scientific contemporaries, took place. There can be little doubt that the fame as an astronomer which Halley ultimately acquired, great as it certainly was, would have been even greater still had it not been somewhat impaired by the misfortune that he had to shine in the same sky as that which was illumined by the unparalleled genius of Newton.

Edmund Halley was born at Haggerston, in the Parish of St. Leonard's, Shoreditch, on October 29th, 1656. His father, who bore the same name as his famous son, was a soap-boiler in Winchester Street, London, and he had conducted his business with such success that he accumulated an ample fortune. I have been unable to obtain more than a very few particulars with respect to the early life of the future astronomer. It would, however, appear that from boyhood he showed considerable aptitude for the acquisition of various kinds of learning, and he also had some capacity for mechanical invention. Halley seems to have received a sound education at St. Paul's School, then under the care of Dr. Thomas Gale.

Here, the young philosopher rapidly distanced his competitors in the various branches of ordinary school instruction. His superiority was, however, most conspicuous in mathematical studies, and, as a natural development of such tastes, we learn that by the time he had left school he had already made good progress in astronomy. At the age of seventeen he was entered as a commoner at Queen's College, Oxford, and the reputation that he brought with him to the University may be inferred from the remark of the writer of "Athenae Ox-onienses," that Halley came to Oxford "with skill in Latin, Greek, and Hebrew, and such a knowledge of geometry as to make a complete dial." Though his studies were thus of a somewhat multifarious nature, yet it is plain that from the first his most favourite pursuit was astronomy. His earliest efforts in practical observation were connected with an eclipse which he observed from his father's house in Winchester Street. It also appears that he had studied theoretical branches of astronomy so far as to be conversant with the application of mathematics to somewhat abstruse problems.

Up to the time of Kepler, philosophers had assumed almost as an axiom that the heavenly bodies must revolve in circles and that the motion of the planet around the orbit which it described must be uniform. We have already seen how that great philosopher, after very persevering labour, succeeded in proving that the orbits of the planets were not circles, but that they were ellipses of small eccentricity. Kepler was, however, unable to shake himself free from the prevailing notion that the angular motion of the planet ought to be of a uniform character around some point. He had indeed proved that the motion round the focus of the ellipse in which the sun lies is not of this description. One of his most important discoveries even related to the fact that at some parts of its orbit a planet swings around the sun with greater angular velocity than at others. But it so happens that in elliptic tracks which differ but little from circles, as is the case with all the more important planetary orbits, the motion round the empty focus of the ellipse is very nearly uniform. It seemed natural to assume, that this was exactly the case, in which event each of the two foci of the ellipse would have had a special significance in relation to the movement of the planet. The youthful Halley, however, demonstrated that so far as the empty focus was concerned, the movement of the planet around it, though so nearly uniform, was still not exactly so, and at the age of nineteen, he published a treatise on the subject which at once placed him in the foremost rank amongst theoretical astronomers.

But Halley had no intention of being merely an astronomer with his pen. He longed to engage in the practical work of observing. He saw that the progress of exact astronomy must depend largely on the determination of the positions of the stars with all attainable accuracy. He accordingly determined to take up this branch of work, which had been so successfully initiated by Tycho Brahe.

At the present day, astronomers of the great national observatories are assiduously engaged in the determination of the places of the stars. A knowledge of the exact positions of these bodies is indeed of the most fundamental importance, not alone for the purposes of scientific astronomy, but also for navigation and for extensive operations of surveying in which accuracy is desired. The fact that Halley determined to concentrate himself on this work shows clearly the scientific acumen of the young astronomer.

Halley, however, found that Hevelius, at Dantzig, and Flamsteed, the Astronomer Royal at Greenwich, were both engaged on work of this character. He accordingly determined to direct his energies in a way that he thought would be more useful to science. He resigned to the two astronomers whom I have named the investigation of the stars in the northern hemisphere, and he sought for himself a field hitherto almost entirely unworked. He determined to go to the southern hemisphere, there to measure and survey those stars which were invisible in Europe, so that his work should supplement the labours of the northern astronomers, and that the joint result of his labours and of theirs might be a complete survey of the most important stars on the surface of the heavens.

In these days, after so many ardent students everywhere have devoted themselves to the study of Nature, it seems difficult for a beginner to find a virgin territory in which to commence his explorations. Halley may, however, be said to have enjoyed the privilege of commencing to work in a magnificent region, the contents of which were previously almost entirely unknown. Indeed none of the stars which were so situated as to have been invisible from Tycho Brahe's observatory at Uraniborg, in Denmark, could be said to have been properly observed. There was, no doubt, a rumour that a Dutchman had observed southern stars from the island of Sumatra, and certain stars were indicated in the southern heavens on a celestial globe. On examination, however, Halley found that no reliance could be placed on the results which had been obtained, so that practically the field before him may be said to have been unworked.

At the age of twenty, without having even waited to take that degree at the university which the authorities would have been glad to confer on so promising an undergraduate, this ardent student of Nature sought his father's permission to go to the southern hemisphere for the purpose of studying the stars which lie around the southern pole. His father possessed the necessary means, and he had likewise the sagacity to encourage the young astronomer. He was indeed most anxious to make everything as easy as possible for so hopeful a son. He provided him with an allowance of 300 pounds a year, which was regarded as a very munificent provision in those days. Halley was also furnished with letters of recommendation from King Charles II., as well as from the directors of the East India Company. He accordingly set sail with his instruments in the year 1676, in one of the East India Company's ships, for the island of St. Helena, which he had selected as the scene of his labours.

After an uneventful voyage of three months, the astronomer landed on St. Helena, with his sextant of five and a half feet radius, and a telescope 24 feet long, and forthwith plunged with ardour into his investigation of the southern skies. He met, however, with one very considerable disappointment. The climate of this island had been represented to him as most favourable for astronomical observation; but instead of the pure blue skies he had been led to expect, he found that they were almost always more or less clouded, and that rain was frequent, so that his observations were very much interrupted. On this account he only remained at St. Helena for a single year, having, during that time, and in spite of many difficulties, accomplished a piece of work which earned for him the title of "our southern Tycho." Thus did Halley establish his fame as an astronomer on the same lonely rock in mid-Atlantic, which nearly a century and a-half later became the scene of Napoleon's imprisonment, when his star, in which he believed so firmly, had irretrievably set.

On his return to England, Halley prepared a map which showed the result of his labours, and he presented it to the king, in 1677. Like his great predecessor Tycho, Halley did not altogether disdain the arts of

HALLEY.

the courtier, for he endeavoured to squeeze a new constellation into the group around the southern pole which he styled "The Royal Oak," adding a description to the effect that the incidents of which "The Royal Oak" was a symbol were of sufficient importance to be inscribed on the surface of the heavens.

There is reason to think that Charles II. duly appreciated the scientific renown which one of his subjects had achieved, and it was probably through the influence of the king that Halley was made a Master of Arts at Oxford on November 18th, 1678. Special reference was made on the occasion to his observations at St. Helena, as evidence of unusual attainments in mathematics and astronomy. This degree was no small honour to such a young man, who, as we have seen, quitted his university before he had the opportunity of graduating in the ordinary manner.

On November 30th, in the same year, the astronomer received a further distinction in being elected a Fellow of the Royal Society. From this time forward he took a most active part in the affairs of the Society, and the numerous papers which he read before it form a very valuable part of that notable series of volumes known as the "Philosophical Transactions." He was subsequently elected to the important office of secretary to the Royal Society, and he discharged the duties of his post until his appointment to Greenwich necessitated his resignation.

Within a year of Halley's election as a Fellow of the Royal Society, he was chosen by the Society to represent them in a discussion which had arisen with Hevelius. The nature of this discussion, or rather the fact that any discussion should have been necessary, may seem strange to modern astronomers, for the point is one on which it would now seem impossible for there to be any difference of opinion. We must, however, remember that the days of Halley were, comparatively speaking, the days of infancy as regards the art of astronomical observation, and issues that now seem obvious were often, in those early times, the occasions of grave and anxious consideration. The particular question on which Halley had to represent the Royal Society may be simply stated. When Tycho Brahe made his memorable investigations into the places of the stars, he had no telescopes to help him. The famous instruments at Uraniborg were merely provided with sights, by which the telescope was pointed to a star on the same principle as a rifle is sighted for a target. Shortly after Tycho's time, Galileo invented the telescope. Of course every one admitted at once the extraordinary advantages which the telescope had to offer, so far as the mere question of the visibility of objects was concerned. But the bearing of Galileo's invention upon what we may describe as the measuring part of astronomy was not so immediately obvious. If a star be visible to the unaided eye, we can determine its place by such instruments as those which Tycho used, in which no telescope is employed. We can, however, also avail ourselves of an instrument in which we view the star not directly but through the intervention of the telescope. Can the place of the star be determined more accurately by the latter method than it can when the telescope is dispensed with? With our present knowledge, of course, there is no doubt about the answer; every one conversant with instruments knows that we can determine the place of a star far more accurately with the telescope than is possible by any mere sighting apparatus. In fact an observer would be as likely to make an error of a minute with the sighting apparatus in Tycho's instrument, as he would be to make an error of a second with the modern telescope, or, to express the matter somewhat differently, we may say, speaking quite generally, that the telescopic method of determining the places of the stars does not lead to errors more than one-sixtieth part as great as which are unavoidable when we make use of Tycho's method.

But though this is so apparent to the modern astronomer, it was not at all apparent in the days of Halley, and accordingly he was sent off to discuss the question with the Continental astronomers. Hevelius, as the representative of the older method, which Tycho had employed with such success, maintained that an instrument could be pointed more accurately at a star by the use of sights than by the use of a telescope, and vigorously disputed the claims put forward by those who believed that the latter method was the more suitable. On May 14th, 1679, Halley started for Dantzig, and the energetic character of the man may be judged from the fact that on the very night of his arrival he commenced to make the necessary observations. In those days astronomical telescopes had only obtained a fractional part of the perfection possessed by the instruments in our modern observatories, and therefore it may not be surprising that the results of the trial were not immediately conclusive. Halley appears to have devoted much time to the investigation; indeed, he remained at Dantzig for more than a twelve-month. On his return to England, he spoke highly of the skill which Hevelius exhibited in the use of his antiquated methods, but Halley was nevertheless too sagacious an observer to be shaken in his preference for the telescopic method of observation.

The next year we find our young astronomer starting for a Continental tour, and we, who complain if the Channel passage lasts more than an hour or two, may note Halley's remark in writing to Hooke on June 15th, 1680: "Having fallen in with bad weather we took forty hours in the journey from Dover to Calais." The scientific distinction which he had already attained was such that he was received in Paris with marked attention. A great deal of his time seems to have been passed in the Paris observatory, where Cassini, the presiding genius, himself an astronomer of well-deserved repute, had extended a hearty welcome to his English visitor. They made observations together of the place of the splendid comet which was then attracting universal attention, and Halley found the work thus done of much use when he subsequently came to investigate the path pursued by this body. Halley was wise enough to spare no pains to derive all possible advantages from his intercourse with the distinguished savants of the French capital. In the further progress of his tour he visited the principal cities of the Continent, leaving behind him everywhere the memory of an amiable disposition and of a rare intelligence.

After Halley's return to England, in 1682, he married a young lady named Mary Tooke, with whom he lived happily, till her death fifty-five years later. On his marriage, he took up his abode in Islington, where he erected his instruments and recommenced his observations.

It has often been the good fortune of astronomers to render practical services to humanity by their investigations, and Halley's achievements in this respect deserve to be noted. A few years after he had settled in England, he published an important paper on the variation of the magnetic compass, for so the departure of the needle from the true north is termed. This subject had indeed early engaged his attention, and he continued to feel much interest in it up to the end of his life. With respect to his labours in this direction, Sir John Herschel says: "To Halley we owe the first appreciation of the real complexity of the subject of magnetism. It is wonderful indeed, and a striking proof of the penetration and sagacity of this extraordinary man, that with his means of information he should have been able to draw such conclusions, and to take so large and comprehensive a view of the subject as he appears to have done." In 1692, Halley explained his theory of terrestrial magnetism, and begged captains of ships to take observations of the variations of the compass in all parts of the world, and to communicate them to the Royal Society, "in order that all the facts may be readily available to those who are hereafter to complete this difficult and complicated subject."

The extent to which Halley was in advance of his contemporaries, in the study of terrestrial magnetism, may be judged from the fact that the subject was scarcely touched after his time till the year 1811. The interest which he felt in it was not of a merely theoretical kind, nor was it one which could be cultivated in an easy-chair. Like all true investigators, he longed to submit his theory to the test of experiment, and for that purpose Halley determined to observe the magnetic variation for himself. He procured from King William III. the command of a vessel called the *Paramour Pink*, with which he started for the South Seas in 1694. This particular enterprise was not, however, successful; for, on crossing the line, some of his men fell sick and one of his lieutenants mutinied, so that he was obliged to return the following year with his mission unaccomplished. The government cashiered the lieutenant, and Halley having procured a second smaller vessel to accompany the "Paramour Pink," started once more in September, 1699. He traversed the Atlantic to the 52nd degree of southern latitude, beyond which his further advance was stopped. "In these latitudes," he writes to say, "we fell in with great islands of ice of so incredible height and magnitude, that I scarce dare write my thoughts of it."

On his return in 1700, Halley published a general chart, showing the variation of the compass at the different places which he had visited. On these charts he set down lines connecting those localities at which the magnetic variation was identical. He thus set an example of the graphic representation of large masses of complex facts, in such a manner as to appeal at once to the eye, a method of which we make many applications in the present day.

But probably the greatest service which Halley ever rendered to human knowledge was the share in which he took in bringing Newton's "Principia" before the world. In fact, as Dr. Glaisher, writing in 1888, has truly remarked, "but for Halley the 'Principia' would not have existed."

It was a visit from Halley in the year 1684 which seems to have first suggested to Newton the idea of publishing the results of his investigations on gravitation. Halley, and other scientific contemporaries, had no doubt some faint glimmering of the great truth which only Newton's genius was able fully to reveal. Halley had indeed shown how, on the assumptions that the planets move in circular orbits round the sun, and that the squares of their periodic times are proportional to the cubes of their mean distances, it may be proved that the force acting on each planet must vary inversely as the square of its distance from the sun. Since, however, each of the planets actually moves in an ellipse, and therefore, at continually varying distances from the sun, it becomes a much more difficult matter to account mathematically for the body's motions on the supposition that the attractive force varies inversely as the square of the distance. This was the question with which Halley found himself confronted, but which his mathematical abilities were not adequate to solve. It would seem that both Hooke and Sir Christopher Wren were interested in the same problem; in fact, the former claimed to have arrived at a solution, but declined to make known his results, giving as an excuse his desire that others having tried and failed might learn to value his achievements all the more. Halley, however, confessed that his attempts at the solution were unsuccessful, and Wren, in order to encourage the other two philosophers to pursue the inquiry, offered to present a book of forty shillings value to either of them who should in the space of two months bring him a convincing proof of it. Such was the value which Sir Christopher set on the Law of Gravitation, upon which the whole fabric of modern astronomy may be said to stand.

Finding himself unequal to the task, Halley went down to Cambridge to see Newton on the subject, and was delighted to learn that the great mathematician had already completed the investigation. He showed Halley that the motions of all the planets could be completely accounted for on the hypothesis of a force of attraction directed towards the sun, which varies inversely as the square of the distance from that body.

Halley had the genius to perceive the tremendous importance of Newton's researches, and he ceased not to urge upon the recluse man of science the necessity for giving his new discoveries publication. He paid another visit to Cambridge with the object of learning more with regard to the mathematical methods which had already conducted Newton to such sublime truths, and he again encouraged the latter both to pursue his investigations, and to give some account of them to the world. In December of the same year Halley had the gratification of announcing to the Royal Society that Newton had promised to send that body a paper containing his researches on Gravitation.

It seems that at this epoch the finances of the Royal Society were at a very low ebb. This impecuniosity was due to the fact that a book by Willoughby, entitled "De Historia Piscium," had been recently printed by the society at great expense. In fact, the coffers were so low that they had some difficulty in paying the salaries of their permanent officials. It appears that the public did not care about the history of fishes, or at all events the volume did not meet with the ready demand which was expected for it. Indeed, it has been recorded that when Halley had undertaken to measure the length of a degree of the earth's surface, at the request of the Royal Society, it was ordered that his expenses be defrayed either in 50 pounds sterling, or in fifty books of fishes. Thus it happened that on June 2nd, the Council, after due consideration of ways and means in connection with the issue of the Principia, "ordered that Halley should undertake the business of looking after the book and printing it at his own charge," which he engaged to do.

It was, as we have elsewhere mentioned, characteristic of Newton that he detested controversies, and he was, in fact, inclined to suppress the third book of the "Principia" altogether rather than have any conflict with Hooke with respect to the discoveries there enunciated. He also thought of changing the name of the work to De Motu Corporum Libri Duo, but upon second thoughts, he retained the original title, remarking, as he wrote to Halley, "It will help the sale of the book, which I ought not to diminish, now it is yours," a sentence which shows conclusively, if further proof were necessary, that Halley had assumed the responsibility of its publication.

Halley spared no pains in pushing forward the publication of his illustrious friend's great work, so that in the same year he was in a position to present a complete copy to King James II., with a proper discourse of his own. Halley also wrote a set of Latin hexameters in praise of Newton's genius, which he printed at the beginning of the work.

The last line of this specimen of Halley's poetic muse may be thus rendered: "Nor mortals nearer may approach the gods."

The intimate friendship between the two greatest astronomers of the time continued without interruption till the death of Newton. It has, indeed, been alleged that some serious cause of estrangement arose between them. There is, however, no satisfactory ground for this statement; indeed, it may be regarded as effectually disposed of by the fact that, in the year 1727, Halley took up the defence of his friend, and wrote two learned papers in support of Newton's "System of Chronology," which had been seriously attacked by a certain ecclesiastic. It is quite evident to any one who has studied these papers that Halley's friendship for Newton was as ardent as ever.

The generous zeal with which Halley adopted and defended the doctrines of Newton with regard to the movements of the celestial bodies was presently rewarded by a brilliant discovery, which has more than any of his other researches rendered his name a familiar one to astronomers. Newton, having explained the movement of the planets, was naturally led to turn his attention to comets. He perceived that their journeyings could be completely accounted for as consequences of the attraction of the sun, and he laid down the principles by which the orbit of a comet could be determined, provided that observations of its positions were obtained at three different dates. The importance of these principles was by no one more quickly recognised than by Halley, who saw at once that it provided the means of detecting something like order in the movements of these strange wanderers. The doctrine of Gravitation seemed to show that just as the planets revolved around the sun in ellipses, so also must the comets. The orbit, however, in the case of the comet, is so extremely elongated that the very small part of the elliptic path within which the comet is both near enough and bright enough to be seen from the earth, is indistinguishable from a parabola. Applying these principles, Halley thought it would be instructive to study the movements of certain bright comets, concerning which reliable observations could be obtained. At the expense of much labour, he laid down the paths pursued by twenty-four of these bodies, which had appeared between the years 1337 and 1698. Amongst them he noticed three, which followed tracks so closely resembling each other, that he was led to conclude the so called three comets could only have been three different appearances of the same body. The first of these occurred in 1531, the second was seen by Kepler in 1607, and the third by Halley himself in 1682. These dates suggested that the observed phenomena might be due to the successive returns of one and the same comet after intervals of seventy-five or seventy-six years. On the further examination of ancient records, Halley found that a comet had been seen in the year 1456, a date, it will be observed, seventy-five years before 1531. Another had been observed seventy-six years earlier than 1456, viz., in 1380, and another seventy-five years before that, in 1305.

As Halley thus found that a comet had been recorded on several occasions at intervals of seventy-five or seventy-six years, he was led to the conclusion that these several apparitions related to one and the same object, which was an obedient vassal of the sun, performing an eccentric journey round that luminary in a period of seventy-five or seventy-six years. To realise the importance of this discovery, it should be remembered that before Halley's time a comet, if not regarded merely as a sign of divine displeasure, or as an omen of intending disaster, had at least been regarded as a chance visitor to the solar system, arriving no one knew whence, and going no one knew whither.

A supreme test remained to be applied to Halley's theory. The question arose as to the date at which this comet would be seen again. We must observe that the question was complicated by the fact that the body, in the course of its voyage around the sun, was exposed to the incessant disturbing action produced by the attraction of the several planets. The comet therefore, does not describe a simple ellipse as it would do if the attraction of the sun were the only force by which its movement were controlled. Each of the planets solicits the comet to depart from its track, and though the amount of these attractions may be insignificant in comparison with the supreme controlling force of the sun, yet the departure from the ellipse is quite sufficient to produce appreciable irregularities in the comet's movement. At the time when Halley lived, no means existed of calculating with precision the effect of the disturbance a comet might experience from the action of the different planets. Halley exhibited his usual astronomical sagacity in deciding that Jupiter would retard the return of the comet to some extent. Had it not been for this disturbance the comet would apparently have been due in 1757 or early in 1758. But the attraction of the great planet would cause delay, so that Halley assigned, for the date of its reappearance, either the end of 1758 or the beginning of 1759. Halley knew that he could not himself live to witness the fulfilment of his prediction, but he says: "If it should return, according to our predictions, about the year 1758, impartial posterity will not refuse to acknowledge that this was first discovered by an Englishman." This was, indeed, a remarkable prediction of an event to occur fifty-three years after it had been uttered. The way in which it was fulfilled forms one of the most striking episodes in the history of astronomy. The comet was first seen on Christmas Day, 1758, and passed through its nearest point to the sun on March 13th, 1759. Halley had then been lying in his grave for seventeen years, yet the verification of his prophecy reflects a glory on his name which will cause it to live for ever in the annals of astronomy. The comet paid a subsequent visit in 1835, and its next appearance is due about 1910.

Halley next entered upon a labour which, if less striking to the imagination than his discoveries with regard to comets, is still of inestimable value in astronomy. He undertook a series of investigations with the object of improving our knowledge of the movements of the planets. This task was practically finished in 1719, though the results of it were not published until after his death in 1749. In the course of it he was led to investigate closely the motion of Venus, and thus he came to recognise for the first time the peculiar importance which attaches to the phenomenon of the transit of this planet across the sun. Halley saw that the transit, which was to take place in the year 1761, would afford a favourable opportunity for determining the distance of the sun, and thus learning the scale of the solar system. He predicted the circumstances of the phenomenon with an astonishing degree of accuracy, considering his means of information, and it is unquestionably to the exertions of Halley in urging the importance of the matter upon astronomers that we owe the unexampled degree of interest taken in the event, and the energy which scientific men exhibited in observing it. The illustrious astronomer had no hope of being himself a witness of the event, for it could not happen till many years after his death. This did not, however, diminish his anxiety to impress upon those who would then be alive, the importance of the occurrence, nor did it lead him to neglect anything which might contribute to the success of the observations. As we now know, Halley rather over-estimated the value of the transit of Venus, as a means of determining the solar distance. The fact is that the circumstances are such that the observation of the time of contact between the edge of the planet and the edge of the sun cannot be made with the accuracy which he had expected.

In 1691, Halley became a candidate for the Savilian Professorship of Astronomy at Oxford. He was not, however, successful, for his candidature was opposed by Flamsteed, the Astronomer Royal of the time, and another was appointed. He received some consolation for this particular disappointment by the fact that, in 1696, owing to Newton's friendly influence, he was appointed deputy Controller of the Mint at Chester, an office which he did not retain for long, as it was abolished two years later. At last, in 1703, he received what he had before vainly sought, and he was appointed to the Savilian chair.

His observations of the eclipse of the sun, which occurred in 1715, added greatly to Halley's reputation. This phenomenon excited special attention, inasmuch as it was the first total eclipse of the sun which had been visible in London since the year 1140. Halley undertook the necessary calculations, and predicted the various circumstances with a far higher degree of precision than the official announcement. He himself observed the phenomenon from the Royal Society's rooms, and he minutely describes the outer atmosphere of the sun, now known as the corona; without, however, offering an opinion as to whether it was a solar or a lunar appendage.

At last Halley was called to the dignified office which he of all men was most competent to fill. On February 9th, 1720, he was appointed Astronomer Royal in succession to Flamsteed. He found things at the Royal Observatory in a most unsatisfactory state. Indeed, there were no instruments, nor anything else that was movable; for such things, being the property of Flamsteed, had been removed by his widow, and though Halley attempted to purchase from that lady some of the instruments which his predecessor had employed, the unhappy personal differences which had existed between him and Flamsteed, and which, as we have already seen, prevented his election as Savilian Professor of Astronomy, proved a bar to the negotiation. Greenwich Observatory wore a very different appearance in those days, from that which the modern visitor, who is fortunate enough to gain admission, may now behold. Not only did Halley find it bereft of instruments, we learn besides that he had no assistants, and was obliged to transact the whole business of the establishment single-handed.

In 1721, however, he obtained a grant of 500 pounds from the Board of Ordnance, and accordingly a transit instrument was erected in the same year. Some time afterwards he procured an eight-foot quadrant, and with these instruments, at the age of sixty-four, he commenced a series of observations on the moon. He intended, if his life was spared, to continue his observations for a period of eighteen years, this being, as astronomers know, a very important cycle in connection with lunar movements. The special object of this vast undertaking was to improve the theory of the moon's motion, so that it might serve more accurately to determine longitudes at sea. This self-imposed task Halley lived to carry to a successful termination, and the tables deduced from his observations, and published after his death, were adopted almost universally by astronomers, those of the French nation being the only exception.

Throughout his life Halley had been singularly free from illness of every kind, but in 1737 he had a stroke of paralysis. Notwithstanding this, however, he worked diligently at his telescope till 1739, after which his health began rapidly to give way. He died on January 14th, 1742, in the eighty-sixth year of his age, retaining his mental faculties to the end. He was buried in the cemetery of the church of Lee in Kent, in the same grave as his wife, who had died five years previously. We are informed by Admiral Smyth that Pond, a later Astronomer Royal, was afterwards laid in the same tomb.

Halley's disposition seems to have been generous and candid, and wholly free from anything like jealousy or rancour. In person he was rather above the middle height, and slight in build; his complexion was fair, and he is said to have always spoken, as well as acted, with uncommon sprightliness. In the eloge pronounced upon him at the Paris Academie Des Sciences, of which Halley had been made a member in 1719 it was said, "he possessed all the qualifications which were necessary to please princes who were desirous of instruction, with a great extent of knowledge and a constant presence of mind; his answers were ready, and at the same time pertinent, judicious, polite and sincere."

Thus we find that Peter the Great was one of his most ardent admirers. He consulted the astronomer on matters connected with shipbuilding, and invited him to his own table. But Halley possessed nobler qualifications than the capacity of pleasing Princes. He was able to excite and to retain the love and admiration of his equals. This was due to the warmth of his attachments, the unselfishness of his devotion to his friends, and to a vein of gaiety and good-humour which pervaded all his conversation.

Greenwich Observatory in Halley's Time.

BRADLEY.

James Bradley was descended from an ancient family in the county of Durham. He was born in 1692 or 1693, at Sherbourne, in Gloucestershire, and was educated in the Grammar School at Northleach. From thence he proceeded in due course to Oxford, where he was admitted a commoner at Balliol College, on March 15th, 1711. Much of his time, while an undergraduate, was passed in Essex with his maternal uncle, the Rev. James Pound, who was a well-known man of science and a diligent observer of the stars. It was doubtless by intercourse with his uncle that young Bradley became so expert in the use of astronomical instruments, but the immortal discoveries he subsequently made show him to have been a born astronomer.

The first exhibition of Bradley's practical skill seems to be contained in two observations which he made in 1717 and 1718. They have been published by Halley, whose acuteness had led him to perceive the extraordinary scientific talents of the young astronomer. Another illustration of the sagacity which Bradley manifested, even at the very commencement of his astronomical career, is contained in a remark of Halley's, who says: "Dr. Pound and his nephew, Mr. Bradley, did, myself being present, in the last opposition of the sun and Mars this way demonstrate the extreme minuteness of the sun's parallax, and that it was not more than twelve seconds nor less than nine seconds." To make the significance of this plain, it should be observed that the determination of the sun's parallax is equivalent to the determination of the distance from the earth to the sun. At the time of which we are now writing, this very important unit of celestial measurement was only very imperfectly known, and the observations of Pound and Bradley may be interpreted to mean that, from their observations, they had come to the conclusion that the distance from the earth to the sun must be more than 94 millions of miles, and less than 125 millions. We now, of course, know that they were not exactly right, for the true distance of the sun is about 93 millions of miles. We cannot, however, but think that it was a very remarkable approach for the veteran astronomer and his brilliant nephew to make towards the determination of a magnitude which did not become accurately known till fifty years later.

Among the earliest parts of astronomical work to which Bradley's attention was directed, were the eclipses of Jupiter's satellites. These phenomena are specially attractive inasmuch as they can be so readily observed, and Bradley found it extremely interesting to calculate the times at which the eclipses should take place, and then to compare his observations with the predicted times. From the success that he met with in this work, and from his other labours, Bradley's reputation as an astronomer increased so greatly that on November the 6th, 1718, he was elected a Fellow of the Royal Society.

Up to this time the astronomical investigations of Bradley had been more those of an amateur than of a professional astronomer, and as it did not at first seem likely that scientific work would lead to any permanent provision, it became necessary for the youthful astronomer to choose a profession. It had been all along intended that he should enter the Church, though for some reason which is not told us, he did not take orders as soon as his age would have entitled him to do so. In 1719, however, the Bishop of Hereford offered Bradley the Vicarage of Bridstow, near Ross, in Monmouthshire, and on July 25th, 1720, he having then taken priest's orders, was duly instituted in his vicarage. In the beginning of the next year, Bradley had some addition to his income from the proceeds of a Welsh living, which, being a sinecure, he was able to hold with his appointment at Bridstow. It appears, however, that his clerical occupations were not very exacting in their demands upon his time, for he was still able to pay long and often-repeated visits to his uncle at Wandsworth, who, being himself a clergyman, seems to have received occasional assistance in his ministerial duties from his astronomical nephew.

The time, however, soon arrived when Bradley was able to make a choice between continuing to exercise his profession as a divine, or devoting himself to a scientific career. The Savilian Professorship of Astronomy in the University of Oxford became vacant by the death of Dr. John Keill. The statutes forbade that the Savilian Professor should also hold a clerical appointment, and Mr. Pound would certainly have been elected to the professorship had he consented to surrender his preferments in the Church. But Pound was unwilling to sacrifice his clerical position, and though two or three other candidates appeared in the field, yet the talents of Bradley were so conspicuous that he was duly elected, his willingness to resign the clerical profession having been first ascertained.

There can be no doubt that, with such influential friends as Bradley possessed, he would have made great advances had he adhered to his profession as a divine. Bishop Hoadly, indeed, with other marks of favour, had already made the astronomer his chaplain. The engrossing nature of Bradley's interest in astronomy decided him, however, to sacrifice all other prospects in comparison with the opening afforded by the Savilian Professorship. It was not that Bradley found himself devoid of interest in clerical matters, but he felt that the true scope for such abilities as he possessed would be better found in the discharge of the scientific duties of the Oxford chair than in the spiritual charge of a parish. On April the 26th, 1722, Bradley read his inaugural lecture in that new position on which he was destined to confer such lustre.

It must, of course, be remembered that in those early days the art of constructing the astronomical telescope was very imperfectly understood. The only known method for getting over the peculiar difficulties presented in the construction of the refracting telescope, was to have it of the most portentous length. In fact, Bradley made several of his observations with an instrument of two hundred and twelve feet focus. In such a case, no tube could be used, and the object glass was merely fixed at the top of a high pole. Notwithstanding the inconvenience and awkwardness of such an instrument, Bradley by its means succeeded in making many careful measurements. He observed, for example, the transit of Mercury over the sun's disc, on October 9th, 1723; he also observed the dimensions of the planet Venus, while a comet which Halley discovered on October the 9th, 1723, was assiduously observed at Wanstead up to the middle of the ensuing month. The first of Bradley's remarkable contributions to the "Philosophical

Transactions" relates to this comet, and the extraordinary amount of work that he went through in connection therewith may be seen from an examination of his book of Calculations which is still extant.

The time was now approaching when Bradley was to make the first of those two great discoveries by which his name has acquired a lustre that has placed him in the very foremost rank of astronomical discoverers. As has been often the case in the history of science, the first of these great successes was attained while he was pursuing a research intended for a wholly different purpose. It had long been recognised that as the earth describes a vast orbit, nearly two hundred million miles in diameter, in its annual journey round the sun, the apparent places of the stars should alter, to some extent, in correspondence with the changes in the earth's position. The nearer the star the greater the shift in its apparent place on the heavens, which must arise from the fact that it was seen from different positions in the earth's orbit. It had been pointed out that these apparent changes in the places of the stars, due to the movement of the earth, would provide the means of measuring the distances of the stars. As, however, these distances are enormously great in comparison with the orbit which the earth describes around the sun, the attempt to determine the distances of the stars by the shift in their positions had hitherto proved ineffectual. Bradley determined to enter on this research once again; he thought that by using instruments of greater power, and by making measurements of increased delicacy, he would be able to perceive and to measure displacements which had proved so small as to elude the skill of the other astronomers who had previously made efforts in the same direction. In order to simplify the investigation as much as possible, Bradley devoted his attention to one particular star, Beta Draconis, which happened to pass near his zenith. The object of choosing a star in this position was to avoid the difficulties which would be introduced by refraction had the star occupied any other place in the heavens than that directly overhead.

We are still able to identify the very spot on which the telescope stood which was used in this memorable research. It was erected at the house then occupied by Molyneux, on the western extremity of Kew Green. The focal length was 24 feet 3 inches, and the eye-glass was 3 and a half feet above the ground floor. The instrument was first set up on November 26th, 1725. If there had been any appreciable disturbance in the place of Beta Draconis in consequence of the movement of the earth around the sun, the star must appear to have the smallest latitude when in conjunction with the sun, and the greatest when in opposition. The star passed the meridian at noon in December, and its position was particularly noticed by Molyneux on the third of that month. Any perceptible displacement by parallax—for so the apparent change in position, due to the earth's motion, is called—would would have made the star shift towards the north. Bradley, however, when observing it on the 17th, was surprised to find that the apparent place of the star, so far from shifting towards the north, as they had perhaps hoped it would, was found to lie a little more to the south than when it was observed before. He took extreme care to be sure that there was no mistake in his observation, and, true astronomer as he was, he scrutinized with the utmost minuteness all the circumstances of the adjustment of his instruments. Still the star went to the south, and it continued so advancing in the same direction until the following March, by which time it had moved no less than twenty seconds south from the place which it occupied when the first observation was made. After a brief pause, in which no apparent movement was perceptible, the star by the middle of April appeared to be returning to the north. Early in June it reached the same distance from the zenith which it had in December. By September the star was as much as thirty-nine seconds more to the north than it had been in March, then it returned towards the south, regaining in December the same situation which it had occupied twelve months before.

This movement of the star being directly opposite to the movements which would have been the consequence of parallax, seemed to show that even if the star had any parallax its effects upon the apparent place were entirely masked by a much larger motion of a totally different description. Various attempts were made to account for the phenomenon, but they were not successful. Bradley accordingly determined to investigate the whole subject in a more thorough manner. One of his objects was to try whether the same movements which he had observed in one star were in any similar degree possessed by other stars. For this purpose he set up a new instrument at Wanstead, and there he commenced a most diligent scrutiny of the apparent places of several stars which passed at different distances from the zenith. He found in the course of this research that other stars exhibited movements of a similar description to those which had already proved so perplexing. For a long time the cause of these apparent movements seemed a mystery. At last, however, the explanation of these remarkable phenomena dawned upon him, and his great discovery was made.

One day when Bradley was out sailing he happened to remark that every time the boat was laid on a different tack the vane at the top of the boat's mast shifted a little, as if there had been a slight change in the direction of the wind. After he had noticed this three or four times he made a remark to the sailors to the effect that it was very strange the wind should always happen to change just at the moment when the boat was going about. The sailors, however, said there had been no change in the wind, but that the alteration in the vane was due to the fact that the boat's course had been altered. In fact, the position of the vane was determined both by the course of the boat and the direction of the wind, and if either of these were altered there would be a corresponding change in the direction of the vane. This meant, of course, that the observer in the boat which was moving along would feel the wind coming from a point different from that in which the wind appeared to be blowing when the boat was at rest, or when it was sailing in some different direction. Bradley's sagacity saw in this observation the clue to the Difficulty which had so long troubled him.

It had been discovered before the time of Bradley that the passage of light through space is not an instantaneous phenomenon. Light requires time for its journey. Galileo surmised that the sun may have reached the horizon before we see it there, and it was indeed sufficiently obvious that a physical action, like the transmission of light, could hardly take place without requiring some lapse of time. The speed with which light actually travelled was, however, so rapid that its determination eluded all the means of experimenting which were available in those days. The penetration of Roemer had previously detected irregularities in the observed times of the eclipses of Jupiter's satellites, which were undoubtedly due to the interval which light required for stretching across the interplanetary spaces. Bradley argued that as light can only travel with a certain speed, it may in a measure be regarded like the wind, which he noticed in the boat. If the observer were at rest, that is to say, if the earth were a stationary object, the direction in which the light actually does come would be different from that in which it appears to come when the earth is in motion. It is true that the earth travels but eighteen miles a second, while the velocity with which light is borne along attains to as much as 180,000 miles a second. The velocity of light is thus ten thousand times greater than the speed of the earth. But even though the wind blew ten thousand times faster than the speed with which the boat was sailing there would still be some change, though no doubt a very small change, in the position of the vane when the boat was in progress from the position it would have if the boat were at rest. It therefore occurred to this most acute of astronomers that when the telescope was pointed towards a star so as to place it apparently in the centre of the field of view, yet it was not generally the true position of the star. It was not, in fact, the position in which the star would have been observed had the earth been at rest. Provided with this suggestion, he explained the apparent movements of the stars by the principle known as the "aberration of light." Every circumstance was accounted for as a consequence of the relative movements of the earth and of the light from the star. This beautiful discovery not only established in the most forcible manner the nature of the movement of light; not only did it illustrate the truth of the Copernican theory which asserted that the earth revolved around the sun, but it was also of the utmost importance in the improvement of practical astronomy. Every observer now knows that, generally speaking, the position which the star appears to have is not exactly the position in which the star does actually lie. The observer is, however, able, by the application of the principles which Bradley so clearly laid down, to apply to an observation the correction which is necessary to obtain from it the true place in which the object is actually situated. This memorable achievement at once conferred on Bradley the highest astronomical fame. He tested his discovery in every way, but only to confirm its truth in the most complete manner.

Halley, the Astronomer Royal, died on the 14th, January, 1742, and Bradley was immediately pointed out as his successor. He was accordingly appointed Astronomer Royal in February, 1742. On first taking up his abode at Greenwich he was unable to conduct his observations owing to the wretched condition in which he found the instruments. He devoted himself, however, assiduously to their repair, and his first transit observation is recorded on the 25th July, 1742. He worked with such energy that on one day it appears that 255 transit observations were taken by himself alone, and in September, 1747, he had completed the series of observations which established his second great discovery, the nutation of the earth's axis. The way in which he was led to the detection of the nutation is strikingly illustrative of the extreme care with which Bradley conducted his observations. He found that in the course of a twelve-month, when the star had completed the movement which was due to aberration, it did not return exactly to the same position which it had previously occupied. At first he thought this must be due to some instrumental error, but after closer examination and repeated study of the effect as manifested by many different stars, he came to the conclusion that its origin must be sought in some quite different source. The fact is that a certain change takes place in the apparent position of the stars which is not due to the movement of the star itself, but is rather to be attributed to changes in the points from which the star's positions are measured.

We may explain the matter in this way. As the earth is not a sphere, but has protuberant parts at the equator, the attraction of the moon exercises on those protuberant parts a pulling effect which continually changes the direction of the earth's axis, and consequently the position of the pole must be in a state of incessant fluctuation. The pole to which the earth's axis points on the sky is, therefore, slowly changing. At present it happens to lie near the Pole Star, but it will not always remain there. It describes a circle around the pole of the Ecliptic, requiring about 25,000 years for a complete circuit. In the course of its progress the pole will gradually pass now near one star and now near another, so that many stars will in the lapse of ages discharge the various functions which the present Pole Star does for us. In about 12,000 years, for instance, the pole will have come near the bright star, Vega. This movement of the pole had been known for ages. But what Bradley discovered was that the pole, instead of describing an uniform movement as had been previously supposed, followed a sinuous course now on one side and now on the other of its mean place. This he traced to the fluctuations of the moon's orbit, which undergoes a continuous change in a period of nineteen years. Thus the efficiency with which the moon acts on the protuberant mass of the earth varies, and thus the pole is caused to oscillate.

This subtle discovery, if perhaps in some ways less impressive than Bradley's earlier achievements of the detection of the aberration of light, is regarded by astronomers as testifying even in a higher degree to his astonishing care and skill as an observer, and justly entitles him to a unique place among the astronomers whose discoveries have been effected by consummate practical skill in the use of astronomical instruments.

Of Bradley's private or domestic life there is but little to tell. In 1744, soon after he became Astronomer Royal, he married a daughter of Samuel Peach, of Chalford, in Gloucestershire. There was but one child, a daughter, who became the wife of her cousin, Rev. Samuel Peach, rector of Compton, Beauchamp, in Berkshire.

Bradley's last two years of life were clouded by a melancholy depression of spirits, due to an apprehension that he should survive his rational faculties. It seems, however, that the ill he dreaded never came upon him, for he retained his mental powers to the close. He died on 13th July, 1762, aged seventy, and was buried at Michinghamton.

WILLIAM HERSCHEL.

William Herschel, one of the greatest astronomers that has ever lived, was born at Hanover, on the 15th November, 1738. His father, Isaac Herschel, was a man evidently of considerable ability, whose life was devoted to the study and practice of music, by which he earned a somewhat precarious maintenance. He had but few worldly goods to leave to his children, but he more than compensated for this by bequeathing to them a splendid inheritance of genius. Touches of genius were, indeed, liberally scattered among the members of Isaac's large family, and in the case of his forth child, William, and of a sister several years younger, it was united with that determined perseverance and rigid adherence to principle which enabled genius to fulfil its perfect work.

A faithful chronicler has given us an interesting account of the way in which Isaac Herschel educated his sons; the narrative is taken from the recollections of one who, at the time we are speaking of, was an unnoticed little girl five or six years old. She writes:—

"My brothers were often introduced as solo performers and assistants in the orchestra at the Court, and I remember that I was frequently prevented from going to sleep by the lively criticisms on music on coming from a concert. Often I would keep myself awake that I might listen to their animating remarks, for it made me so happy to see them so happy. But generally their conversation would branch out on philosophical subjects, when my brother William and my father often argued with such warmth that my mother's interference became necessary, when the names—Euler, Leibnitz, and Newton—sounded rather too loud for the repose of her little ones, who had to be at school by seven in the morning." The child whose reminiscences are here given became afterwards the famous Caroline Herschel. The narrative of her life, by Mrs. John Herschel, is a most interesting book, not only for the account it contains of the remarkable woman herself, but also because it provides the best picture we have of the great astronomer to whom Caroline devoted her life.

This modest family circle was, in a measure, dispersed at the outbreak of the Seven Years' War in 1756. The French proceeded to invade Hanover, which, it will be remembered, belonged at this time to the British dominions. Young William Herschel had already obtained the position of a regular performer in the regimental band of the Hanoverian Guards, and it was his fortune to obtain some experience of actual warfare in the disastrous battle of Hastenbeck. He was not wounded, but he had to spend the night after the battle in a ditch, and his meditations on the occasion convinced him that soldiering was not the profession exactly adapted to his tastes. We need not attempt to conceal the fact that he left his regiment by the very simple but somewhat risky process of desertion. He had, it would seem, to adopt disguises to effect his escape. At all events, by some means he succeeded in eluding detection and reached England in safety. It is interesting to have learned on good authority that many years after this offence was committed it was solemnly forgiven. When Herschel had become the famous astronomer, and as such visited King George at Windsor, the King at their first meeting handed to him his pardon for deserting from the army, written out in due form by his Majesty himself.

It seems that the young musician must have had some difficulty in providing for his maintenance during the first few years of his abode in England. It was not until he had reached the age of twenty-two that he succeeded in obtaining any regular appointment. He was then made Instructor of Music to the Durham Militia. Shortly afterwards, his talents being more widely recognised, he was appointed as organist at the parish church at Halifax, and his prospects in life now being fairly favourable, and the Seven Years' War being over, he ventured to pay a visit to Hanover to see his father. We can imagine the delight with which old Isaac Herschel welcomed his promising son, as well as his parental pride when a concert was given at which some of William's compositions were performed. If the father was so intensely gratified on this occasion, what would his feelings have been could he have lived to witness his son's future career? But this pleasure was not to be his, for he died many years before William became an astronomer.

In 1766, about a couple of years after his return to England from This visit to his old home, we find that Herschel had received a further promotion to be organist in the Octagon Chapel, at Bath. Bath was then, as now, a highly fashionable resort, and many notable personages patronised the rising musician. Herschel had other points in his favour besides his professional skill; his appearance was good, his address was prepossessing, and even his nationality was a distinct advantage, inasmuch as he was a Hanoverian in the reign of King George the Third. On Sundays he played the organ, to the great delight of the congregation, and on week-days he was occupied by giving lessons to private

19, New King Street, Bath, where Herschel lived.

pupils, and in preparation for public performances. He thus came to be busily employed, and seems to have been in the enjoyment of comfortable means.

From his earliest youth Herschel had been endowed with that invaluable characteristic, an eager curiosity for knowledge. He was naturally desirous of perfecting himself in the theory of music, and thus he was led to study mathematics. When he had once tasted the charms of mathematics, he saw vast regions of knowledge unfolded before him, and in this way he was induced to direct his attention to astronomy. More and more this pursuit seems to have engrossed his attention, until at last it had become an absorbing passion. Herschel was, however, still obliged, by the exigency of procuring a livelihood, to give up the

WILLIAM HERSCHEL.

best part of his time to his profession as a musician; but his heart was eagerly fixed on another science, and every spare moment was steadily devoted to astronomy. For many years, however, he continued to labour at his original calling, nor was it until he had attained middle age and become the most celebrated astronomer of the time, that he was enabled to concentrate his attention exclusively on his favourite pursuit.

It was with quite a small telescope which had been lent him by a friend that Herschel commenced his career as an observer. However, he speedily discovered that to see all he wanted to see, a telescope of far greater power would be necessary, and he determined to obtain this more powerful instrument by actually making it with his own hands.

CAROLINE HERSCHEL.

At first it may seem scarcely likely that one whose occupation had previously been the study and practice of music should meet with success
in so technical an operation as the construction of a telescope. It may,
however, be mentioned that the kind of instrument which Herschel
designed to construct was formed on a very different principle from
the refracting telescopes with which we are ordinarily familiar. His
telescope was to be what is termed a reflector. In this type of instrument the optical power is obtained by the use of a mirror at the bottom
of the tube, and the astronomer looks down through the tube TO-
WARDS HIS MIRROR and views the reflection of the stars with its
aid. Its efficiency as a telescope depends entirely on the accuracy with
which the requisite form has been imparted to the mirror. The surface

has to be hollowed out a little, and this has to be done so truly that the slightest deviation from good workmanship in this essential particular would be fatal to efficient performance of the telescope.

The mirror that Herschel employed was composed of a mixture of two parts of copper to one of tin; the alloy thus obtained is an intensely hard material, very difficult to cast into the proper shape, and very difficult to work afterwards. It possesses, however, when polished, a lustre hardly inferior to that of silver itself. Herschel has recorded hardly any particulars as to the actual process by which he cast and figured his reflectors. We are however, told that in later years, after his telescopes had become famous, he made a considerable sum of money by the manufacture and sale of great instruments. Perhaps this may be the reason why he never found it expedient to publish any very explicit details as to the means by which his remarkable successes were obtained.

Since Herschel's time many other astronomers, notably the late Earl of Rosse, have experimented in the same direction, and succeeded in making telescopes certainly far greater, and probably more perfect, than any which Herschel appears to have constructed. The details of these later methods are now well known, and have been extensively practised. Many amateurs have thus been able to make telescopes by following the instructions so clearly laid down by Lord Rosse and the other authorities. Indeed, it would seem that any one who has a little mechanical skill and a good deal of patience ought now to experience no great difficulty in constructing a telescope quite as powerful as that which first brought Herschel into fame. I should, however, mention that in these modern days the material generally used for the mirror is of a more tractable description than the metallic substance which was employed by Herschel and by Lord Rosse. A reflecting telescope of the present day would not be fitted with a mirror composed of that alloy known as speculum metal, whose composition I have already mentioned. It has been found more advantageous to employ a glass mirror carefully figured and polished, just as a metallic mirror would have been, and then to impart to the polished glass surface a fine coating of silver laid down by a chemical process. The silver-on-glass mirrors are so much lighter and so much easier to construct that the more old-fashioned metallic mirrors may be said to have fallen into almost total disuse. In one respect however, the metallic mirror may still claim the advantage that, with reasonable care, its surface will last bright and untarnished for a much longer period than can the silver film on the glass. However, the operation of re-silvering a glass has now become such a simple one that the advantage this indicates is not relatively so great as might at first be supposed.

Some years elapsed after Herschel's attention had been first directed to astronomy, before he reaped the reward of his exertions in the possession of a telescope which would adequately reveal some of the

STREET VIEW, HERSCHEL HOUSE, SLOUGH.

glories of the heavens. It was in 1774, when the astronomer was thirty-six years old, that he obtained his first glimpse of the stars with an instrument of his own construction. Night after night, as soon as his musical labours were ended, his telescopes were brought out, sometimes into the small back garden of his house at Bath, and sometimes into the street in front of his hall-door. It was characteristic of him that he was always endeavouring to improve his apparatus. He was incessantly making fresh mirrors, or trying new lenses, or combinations of lenses to act as eye-pieces, or projecting alterations in the mounting by which the telescope was supported. Such was his enthusiasm that his house, we are told, was incessantly littered with the usual indications of the workman's presence, greatly to the distress of his sister, who, at this time, had come to take up her abode with him and look after his housekeeping. Indeed, she complained that in his astronomical ardour he sometimes omitted to take off, before going into his workshop, the beautiful lace ruffles which he wore while conducting a concert, and that consequently they became soiled with the pitch employed in the polishing of his mirrors.

This sister, who occupies such a distinct place in scientific history is the same little girl to whom we have already referred. From her earliest days she seems to have cherished a passionate admiration for her brilliant brother William. It was the proudest delight of her childhood as well as of her mature years to render him whatever service she could; no man of science was ever provided with a more capable or energetic helper than William Herschel found in this remarkable woman. Whatever work had to be done she was willing to bear her share in it, or even to toil at it unassisted if she could be allowed to do so. She not only managed all his domestic affairs, but in the grinding of the lenses and in the polishing of the mirrors she rendered every assistance that was possible. At one stage of the very delicate operation of fashioning a reflector, it is necessary for the workman to remain with his hand on the mirror for many hours in succession. When such labours were in progress, Caroline used to sit by her brother, and enliven the time by reading stories aloud, sometimes pausing to feed him with a spoon while his hands were engaged on the task from which he could not desist for a moment.

When mathematical work had to be done Caroline was ready for it; she had taught herself sufficient to enable her to perform the kind of calculations, not, perhaps, very difficult ones, that Herschel's work required; indeed, it is not too much to say that the mighty life-work which this man was enabled to perform could never have been accomplished had it not been for the self-sacrifice of this ever-loving and faithful sister. When Herschel was at the telescope at night, Caroline sat by him at her desk, pen in hand, ready to write down the notes of the observations as they fell from her brother's lips. This was no insignificant toil. The telescope was, of course, in the open air, and as

Herschel not unfrequently continued his observations throughout the whole of a long winter's night, there were but few women who could have accomplished the task which Caroline so cheerfully executed. From dusk till dawn, when the sky was clear, were Herschel's observing hours, and what this sometimes implied we can realise from the fact that Caroline assures us she had sometimes to desist because the ink had actually frozen in her pen. The night's work over, a brief rest was taken, and while William had his labours for the day to attend to,

GARDEN VIEW, HERSCHEL HOUSE, SLOUGH.

Caroline carefully transcribed the observations made during the night before, reduced all the figures and prepared everything in readiness for the observations that were to follow on the ensuing evening.

But we have here been anticipating a little of the future which lay before the great astronomer; we must now revert to the history of his early work, at Bath, in 1774, when Herschel's scrutiny of the skies first commenced with an instrument of his own manufacture. For some few years he did not attain any result of importance; no doubt he made a few interesting observations, but the value of the work during those years is to be found, not in any actual discoveries which were accomplished, but in the practice which Herschel obtained in the use of his instruments. It was not until 1782 that the great achievement took place by which he at once sprang into fame.

It is sometimes said that discoveries are made by accident, and, no doubt, to a certain extent, but only, I fancy to a very small extent, this statement may be true. It is, at all events, certain that such lucky accidents do not often fall to the lot of people unless those people have done much to deserve them. This was certainly the case with Herschel. He appears to have formed a project for making a close examination of all the stars above a certain magnitude. Perhaps he intended to confine this research to a limited region of the sky, but, at all events, he seems to have undertaken the work energetically and systematically. Star after star was brought to the centre of the field of view of his telescope, and after being carefully examined was then displaced, while another star was brought forward to be submitted to the same process. In the great majority of cases such observations yield really nothing of importance; no doubt even the smallest star in the heavens would, if we could find out all about it, reveal far more than all the astronomers that were ever on the earth have even conjectured. What we actually learn about the great majority of stars is only information of the most meagre description. We see that the star is a little point of light, and we see nothing more.

In the great review which Herschel undertook he doubtless examined hundreds, or perhaps thousands of stars, allowing them to pass away without note or comment. But on an ever-memorable night in March, 1782, it happened that he was pursuing his task among the stars in the Constellation of Gemini. Doubtless, on that night, as on so many other nights, one star after another was looked at only to be dismissed, as not requiring further attention. On the evening in question, however, one star was noticed which, to Herschel's acute vision seemed different from the stars which in so many thousands are strewn over the sky. A star properly so called appears merely as a little point of light, which no increase of magnifying power will ever exhibit with a true disc. But there was something in the star-like object which Herschel saw that immediately arrested his attention and made him apply to it a higher magnifying power. This at once disclosed the fact that the object possessed a disc, that is, a definite, measurable size, and that it was thus totally different from any one of the hundreds and thousands of stars which exist elsewhere in space. Indeed, we may say at once that this little object was not a star at all; it was a planet. That such was its true nature was confirmed, after a little further observation, by perceiving that the body was shifting its place on the heavens relatively to the stars. The organist at the Octagon Chapel at Bath had, therefore, discovered a new planet with his home-made telescope.

I can imagine some one will say, "Oh, there was nothing so wonderful in that; are not planets always being discovered? Has not M. Palisa, for instance, discovered about eighty of such objects, and are there not hundreds of them known nowadays?" This is, to a certain extent, quite true. I have not the least desire to detract from the credit of those industrious and sharp-sighted astronomers who have in modern days brought so many of these little objects within our cognisance. I think, however, it must be admitted that such discoveries have a totally different importance in the history of science from that which belongs to the peerless achievement of Herschel. In the first place, it must be observed that the minor planets now brought to light are so minute that if a score of them were rolled to together into one lump it would not be one-thousandth part of the size of the grand planet discovered by Herschel. This is, nevertheless, not the most important point. What marks Herschel's achievement as one of the great epochs in the history of astronomy is the fact that the detection of Uranus was the very first recorded occasion of the discovery of any planet whatever.

For uncounted ages those who watched the skies had been aware of the existence of the five old planets—Jupiter, Mercury, Saturn, Venus, and Mars. It never seems to have occurred to any of the ancient philosophers that there could be other similar objects as yet undetected over and above the well-known five. Great then was the astonishment of the scientific world when the Bath organist announced his discovery that the five planets which had been known from all antiquity must now admit the company of a sixth. And this sixth planet was, indeed, worthy on every ground to be received into the ranks of the five glorious bodies of antiquity. It was, no doubt, not so large as Saturn, it was certainly very much less than Jupiter; on the other hand, the new body was very much larger than Mercury, than Venus, or than Mars, and the earth itself seemed quite an insignificant object in comparison with this newly added member of the Solar System. In one respect, too, Herschel's new planet was a much more imposing object than any one of the older bodies; it swept around the sun in a majestic orbit, far outside that of Saturn, which had previously been regarded as the boundary of the Solar System, and its stately progress required a period of not less than eighty-one years.

VIEW OF THE OBSERVATORY, HERSCHEL HOUSE, SLOUGH.

King George the Third, hearing of the achievements of the Hanoverian musician, felt much interest in his discovery, and accordingly Herschel was bidden to come to Windsor, and to bring with him the famous telescope, in order to exhibit the new planet to the King, and to tell his Majesty all about it. The result of the interview was to give Herschel the opportunity for which he had so long wished, of being able to devote himself exclusively to science for the rest of his life.

The King took so great a fancy to the astronomer that he first, as I have already mentioned, duly pardoned his desertion from the army, some twenty-five years previously. As a further mark of his favour the

King proposed to confer on Herschel the title of his Majesty's own astronomer, to assign to him a residence near Windsor, to provide him with a salary, and to furnish such funds as might be required for the erection of great telescopes, and for the conduct of that mighty scheme of celestial observation on which Herschel was so eager to enter. Herschel's capacity for work would have been much impaired if he had been deprived of the aid of his admirable sister, and to her, therefore,

THE 40FT. TELESCOPE WAS IT WAS IN THE YEAR 1863, HERSCHEL HOUSE, SLOUGH.

the King also assigned a salary, and she was installed as Herschel's assistant in his new post.

With his usually impulsive determination, Herschel immediately cut himself free from all his musical avocations at Bath, and at once entered on the task of making and erecting the great telescopes at Windsor. There, for more than thirty years, he and his faithful sister prosecuted with unremitting ardour their nightly scrutiny of the sky. Paper after paper was sent to the Royal Society, describing the hundreds, indeed the thousands, of objects such as double stars; nebulae and clusters, which were first revealed to human gaze during those midnight vigils. To the end of his life he still continued at every possible opportunity to devote himself to that beloved pursuit in which he had such unparalleled success. No single discovery of Herschel's later years was, however, of the same momentous description as that which first brought him to fame.

Herschel married when considerably advanced in life and he lived to enjoy the indescribable pleasure of finding that his only son, afterwards Sir John Herschel, was treading worthily in his footsteps, and attaining renown as an astronomical observer, second only to that of his father. The elder Herschel died in 1822, and his illustrious sister Caroline then returned to Hanover, where she lived for many years to receive the respect and attention which were so justly hers. She died at a very advanced age in 1848.

LAPLACE.

The author of the "Mecanique Celeste" was born at Beaumont-en-Auge, near Honfleur, in 1749, just thirteen years later than his renowned friend Lagrange. His father was a farmer, but appears to have been in a position to provide a good education for a son who seemed promising. Considering the unorthodoxy in religious matters which is generally said to have characterized Laplace in later years, it is interesting to note that when he was a boy the subject which first claimed his attention was theology. He was, however, soon introduced to the study of mathematics, in which he presently became so proficient, that while he was still no more than eighteen years old, he obtained employment as a mathematical teacher in his native town.

Desiring wider opportunities for study and for the acquisition of fame than could be obtained in the narrow associations of provincial life, young Laplace started for Paris, being provided with letters of introduction to D'Alembert, who then occupied the most prominent position as a mathematician in France, if not in the whole of Europe. D'Alembert's fame was indeed so brilliant that Catherine the Great wrote to ask him to undertake the education of her Son, and promised the splendid income of a hundred thousand francs. He preferred, however, a quiet life of research in Paris, although there was but a modest salary attached to his office. The philosopher accordingly declined the alluring offer to go to Russia, even though Catherine wrote again to say: "I know that your refusal arises from your desire to cultivate your studies and your friendships in quiet. But this is of no consequence: bring all your friends with you, and I promise you that both you and they shall have every accommodation in my power." With equal firmness the illustrious mathematician resisted the manifold attractions with which Frederick the Great sought to induce him, to take up his residence at Berlin. In reading of these invitations we cannot but be struck at the extraordinary respect which was then paid to scientific distinction. It must be remembered that the discoveries of such a man as D'Alembert were utterly incapable of being appreciated except by those who possessed a high degree of mathematical culture. We nevertheless find the potentates of Russia and Prussia entreating and, as it happens, vainly entreating, the most distinguished mathematician in France to accept the positions that they were proud to offer him.

It was to D'Alembert, the profound mathematician, that young Laplace, the son of the country farmer, presented his letters of introduction. But those letters seem to have elicited no reply, whereupon Laplace wrote to D'Alembert submitting a discussion on some point in Dynamics. This letter instantly produced the desired effect. D'Alembert thought that such mathematical talent as the young man displayed was in itself the best of introductions to his favour. It could not be overlooked, and accordingly he invited Laplace to come and see him. Laplace, of course, presented himself, and ere long D'Alembert obtained for the rising philosopher a professorship of mathematics in the Military School in Paris. This gave the brilliant young mathematician the opening for which he sought, and he quickly availed himself of it.

Laplace was twenty-three years old when his first memoir on a profound mathematical subject appeared in the Memoirs of the Academy at Turin. From this time onwards we find him publishing one memoir after another in which he attacks, and in many cases successfully vanquishes, profound difficulties in the application of the Newtonian theory of gravitation to the explanation of the solar system. Like his great contemporary Lagrange, he loftily attempted problems which demanded consummate analytical skill for their solution. The attention of the scientific world thus became riveted on the splendid discoveries which emanated from these two men, each gifted with extraordinary genius.

Laplace's most famous work is, of course, the "Mecanique Celeste," in which he essayed a comprehensive attempt to carry out the principles which Newton had laid down, into much greater detail than Newton had found practicable. The fact was that Newton had not only to construct the theory of gravitation, but he had to invent the mathematical tools, so to speak, by which his theory could be applied to the explanation of the movements of the heavenly bodies. In the course of the century which had elapsed between the time of Newton and the time of Laplace, mathematics had been extensively developed. In particular, that potent instrument called the infinitesimal calculus, which Newton had invented for the investigation of nature, had become so far perfected that Laplace, when he attempted to unravel the movements of the heavenly bodies, found himself provided with a calculus far more efficient than that which had been available to Newton. The purely geometrical methods which Newton employed, though they are admirably adapted for demonstrating in a general way the tendencies of forces and for explaining the more obvious phenomena by which the movements of the heavenly bodies are disturbed, are yet quite inadequate for dealing with the more subtle effects of the Law of Gravitation. The disturbances which one planet exercises upon the rest can only be fully ascertained by the aid of long calculation, and for these calculations analytical methods are required.

With an armament of mathematical methods which had been perfected since the days of Newton by the labours of two or three generations of consummate mathematical inventors, Laplace essayed in the "Mecanique Celeste" to unravel the mysteries of the heavens. It will hardly be disputed that the book which he has produced is one of the most difficult books to understand that has ever been written. In great part, of course, this difficulty arises from the very nature of the subject, and is so far unavoidable. No one need attempt to read the "Mecanique Celeste" who has not been naturally endowed with considerable mathematical aptitude which he has cultivated by years of assiduous study. The critic will also note that there are grave defects in Laplace's method of treatment. The style is often extremely obscure, and the author frequently leaves great gaps in his argument, to the sad discomfiture of his reader. Nor does it mend matters to say, as Laplace often does say, that it is "easy to see" how one step follows from another. Such inferences often present great difficulties even to excellent mathematicians. Tradition indeed tells us that when Laplace had occasion to refer to his own book, it sometimes happened that an argument which he had dismissed with his usual formula, "Il est facile a voir,"

cost the illustrious author himself an hour or two of hard thinking before he could recover the train of reasoning which had been omitted.
But there are certain parts of this great work which have always received the enthusiastic admiration of mathematicians. Laplace has, in
fact, created whole tracts of science, some of which have been subsequently developed with much advantage in the prosecution of the
study of Nature.

Judged by a modern code the gravest defect of Laplace's great work
is rather of a moral than of a mathematical nature. Lagrange and he
advanced together in their study of the mechanics of the heavens, at
one time perhaps along parallel lines, while at other times they pursued
the same problem by almost identical methods. Sometimes the important result was first reached by Lagrange, sometimes it was Laplace
who had the good fortune to make the discovery. It would doubtless
be a difficult matter to draw the line which should exactly separate the
contributions to astronomy made by one of these illustrious mathematicians, and the contributions made by the other. But in his great work
Laplace in the loftiest manner disdained to accord more than the very
barest recognition to Lagrange, or to any of the other mathematicians,
Newton alone excepted, who had advanced our knowledge of the
mechanism of the heavens. It would be quite impossible for a student
who confined his reading to the "Mecanique Celeste" to gather from
any indications that it contains whether the discoveries about which he
was reading had been really made by Laplace himself or whether they
had not been made by Lagrange, or by Euler, or by Clairaut. With our
present standard of morality in such matters, any scientific man who
now brought forth a work in which he presumed to ignore in this
wholesale fashion the contributions of others to the subject on which
he was writing, would be justly censured and bitter controversies
would undoubtedly arise. Perhaps we ought not to judge Laplace by
the standard of our own time, and in any case I do not doubt that
Laplace might have made a plausible defence. It is well known that
when two investigators are working at the same subjects, and constantly publishing their results, it sometimes becomes difficult for each
investigator himself to distinguish exactly between what he has accomplished and that which must be credited to his rival. Laplace may probably have said to himself that he was going to devote his energies to a

great work on the interpretation of Nature, that it would take all his time and all his faculties, and all the resources of knowledge that he could command, to deal justly with the mighty problems before him. He would not allow himself to be distracted by any side issue. He could not tolerate that pages should be wasted in merely discussing to whom we owe each formula, and to whom each deduction from such formula is due. He would rather endeavour to produce as complete a picture as he possibly could of the celestial mechanics, and whether it were by means of his mathematics alone, or whether the discoveries of others may have contributed in any degree to the result, is a matter so infinitesimally insignificant in comparison with the grandeur of his subject that he would altogether neglect it. "If Lagrange should think," Laplace might say, "that his discoveries had been unduly appropriated, the proper course would be for him to do exactly what I have done. Let him also write a "Mecanique Celeste," let him employ those consummate talents which he possesses in developing his noble subject to the utmost. Let him utilise every result that I or any other mathematician have arrived at, but not trouble himself unduly with unimportant historical details as to who discovered this, and who discovered that; let him produce such a work as he could write, and I shall heartily welcome it as a splendid contribution to our science." Certain it is that Laplace and Lagrange continued the best of friends, and on the death of the latter it was Laplace who was summoned to deliver the funeral oration at the grave of his great rival.

The investigations of Laplace are, generally speaking, of too technical a character to make it possible to set forth any account of them in such a work as the present. He did publish, however, one treatise, called the "Systeme du Monde," in which, without introducing mathematical symbols, he was able to give a general account of the theories of the celestial movements, and of the discoveries to which he and others had been led. In this work the great French astronomer sketched for the first time that remarkable doctrine by which his name is probably most generally known to those readers of astronomical books who are not specially mathematicians. It is in the "Systeme du Monde" that Laplace laid down the principles of the Nebular Theory which, in modern days, has been generally accepted by those philosophers who

Laplace.

are competent to judge, as substantially a correct expression of a great historical fact.

The Nebular Theory gives a physical account of the origin of the solar system, consisting of the sun in the centre, with the planets and their attendant satellites. Laplace perceived the significance of the fact that all the planets revolved in the same direction around the sun; he noticed also that the movements of rotation of the planets on their axes were performed in the same direction as that in which a planet revolves around the sun; he saw that the orbits of the satellites, so far at least as he knew them, revolved around their primaries also in the same direction. Nor did it escape his attention that the sun itself rotated on its axis in the same sense. His philosophical mind was led to reflect that such a remarkable unanimity in the direction of the movements in the solar system demanded some special explanation. It would have been in the highest degree improbable that there should have been this unanimity unless there had been some physical reason to account for it. To appreciate the argument let us first concentrate our attention on three particular bodies, namely the earth, the sun, and the moon. First the earth revolves around the sun in a certain direction, and the earth also rotates on its axis. The direction in which the earth turns in accordance with this latter movement might have been that in which it revolves around the sun, or it might of course have been opposite thereto. As a matter of fact the two agree. The moon in its monthly revolution around the earth follows also the same direction, and our satellite rotates on its axis in the same period as its monthly revolution, but in doing so is again observing this same law. We have therefore in the earth and moon four movements, all taking place in the same direction, and this is also identical with that in which the sun rotates once every twenty-five days. Such a coincidence would be very unlikely unless there were some physical reason for it. Just as unlikely would it be that in tossing a coin five heads or five tails should follow each other consecutively. If we toss a coin five times the chances that it will turn up all heads or all tails is but a small one. The probability of such an event is only one-sixteenth.

There are, however, in the solar system many other bodies besides the three just mentioned which are animated by this common movement. Among them are, of course, the great planets, Jupiter, Saturn, Mars, Venus, and Mercury, and the satellites which attend on these planets. All these planets rotate on their axes in the same direction as they revolve around the sun, and all their satellites revolve also in the same way. Confining our attention merely to the earth, the sun, and the five great planets with which Laplace was acquainted, we have no fewer than six motions of revolution and seven motions of rotation, for in the latter we include the rotation of the sun. We have also sixteen satellites of the planets mentioned whose revolutions round their primaries are in the same direction. The rotation of the moon on its axis may also be reckoned, but as to the rotations of the satellites of the other planets we cannot speak with any confidence, as they are too far off to be observed with the necessary accuracy. We have thus thirty circular movements in the solar system connected with the sun and moon and those great planets than which no others were known in the days of Laplace. The significant fact is that all these thirty movements take place in the same direction. That this should be the case without some physical reason would be just as unlikely as that in tossing a coin thirty times it should turn up all heads or all tails every time without exception.

We can express the argument numerically. Calculation proves that such an event would not generally happen oftener than once out of five hundred millions of trials. To a philosopher of Laplace's penetration, who had made a special study of the theory of probabilities, it seemed well-nigh inconceivable that there should have been such unanimity in the celestial movements, unless there had been some adequate reason to account for it. We might, indeed, add that if we were to include all the objects which are now known to belong to the solar system, the argument from probability might be enormously increased in strength. To Laplace the argument appeared so conclusive that he sought for some physical cause of the remarkable phenomenon which the solar system presented. Thus it was that the famous Nebular Hypothesis took its rise. Laplace devised a scheme for the origin of the sun and the planetary system, in which it would be a necessary consequence that all the movements should take place in the same direction as they are actually observed to do.

Let us suppose that in the beginning there was a gigantic mass of nebulous material, so highly heated that the iron and other substances which now enter into the composition of the earth and planets were then suspended in a state of vapour. There is nothing unreasonable in such a supposition indeed, we know as a matter of fact that there are thousands of such nebulae to be discerned at present through our telescopes. It would be extremely unlikely that any object could exist without possessing some motion of rotation; we may in fact assert that for rotation to be entirely absent from the great primeval nebula would be almost infinitely improbable. As ages rolled on, the nebula gradually dispersed away by radiation its original stores of heat, and, in accordance with well-known physical principles, the materials of which it was formed would tend to coalesce. The greater part of those materials would become concentrated in a mighty mass surrounded by outlying uncondensed vapours. There would, however, also be regions throughout the extent of the nebula, in which subsidiary centres of condensation would be found. In its long course of cooling, the nebula would, therefore, tend ultimately to form a mighty central body with a number of smaller bodies disposed around it. As the nebula was initially endowed with a movement of rotation, the central mass into which it had chiefly condensed would also revolve, and the subsidiary bodies would be animated by movements of revolution around the central body. These movements would be all pursued in one common direction, and it follows, from well-known mechanical principles, that each of the subsidiary masses, besides participating in the general revolution around the central body, would also possess a rotation around its axis, which must likewise be performed in the same direction. Around the subsidiary bodies other objects still smaller would be formed, just as they themselves were formed relatively to the great central mass.

As the ages sped by, and the heat of these bodies became gradually dissipated, the various objects would coalesce, first into molten liquid masses, and thence, at a further stage of cooling, they would assume the appearance of solid masses, thus producing the planetary bodies such as we now know them. The great central mass, on account of its preponderating dimensions, would still retain, for further uncounted ages, a large quantity of its primeval heat, and would thus display the splendours of a glowing sun. In this way Laplace was able to account for the remarkable phenomena presented in the movements of the bodies of the solar system. There are many other points also in which the nebular theory is known to tally with the facts of observation. In fact, each advance in science only seems to make it more certain that the Nebular Hypothesis substantially represents the way in which our solar system has grown to its present form.

Not satisfied with a career which should be merely scientific, Laplace sought to connect himself with public affairs. Napoleon appreciated his genius, and desired to enlist him in the service of the State. Accordingly he appointed Laplace to be Minister of the Interior. The experiment was not successful, for he was not by nature a statesman. Napoleon was much disappointed at the ineptitude which the great mathematician showed for official life, and, in despair of Laplace's capacity as an administrator, declared that he carried the spirit of his infinitesimal calculus into the management of business. Indeed, Laplace's political conduct hardly admits of much defence. While he accepted the honours which Napoleon showered on him in the time of his prosperity, he seems to have forgotten all this when Napoleon could no longer render him service. Laplace was made a Marquis by Louis XVIII., a rank which he transmitted to his son, who was born in 1789. During the latter part of his life the philosopher lived in a retired country place at Arcueile. Here he pursued his studies, and by strict abstemiousness, preserved himself from many of the infirmities of old age. He died on March the 5th, 1827, in his seventy-eighth year, his last words being, "What we know is but little, what we do not know is immense."

BRINKLEY.

Provost Baldwin held absolute sway in the University of Dublin for forty-one years. His memory is well preserved there. The Bursar still dispenses the satisfactory revenues which Baldwin left to the College. None of us ever can forget the marble angels round the figure of the dying Provost on which we used to gaze during the pangs of the Examination Hall.

Baldwin died in 1785, and was succeeded by Francis Andrews, a Fellow of seventeen years' standing. As to the scholastic acquirements of Andrews, all I can find is a statement that he was complimented by the polite Professors of Padua on the elegance and purity with which he discoursed to them in Latin. Andrews was also reputed to be a skilful lawyer. He was certainly a Privy Councillor and a prominent member of the Irish House of Commons, and his social qualities were excellent. Perhaps it was Baldwin's example that stimulated a desire in Andrews to become a benefactor to his college. He accordingly bequeathed a sum of 3,000 pounds and an annual income of 250 pounds wherewith to build and endow an astronomical Observatory in the University. The figures just stated ought to be qualified by the words of cautious Ussher (afterwards the first Professor of Astronomy), that "this money was to arise from an accumulation of a part of his property, to commence upon a particular contingency happening to his family." The astronomical endowment was soon in jeopardy by litigation. Andrews thought he had provided for his relations by leaving to them certain leasehold interests connected with the Provost's estate. The law courts, however, held that these interests were not at the disposal of the testator, and handed them over to Hely Hutchinson, the next Provost. The disappointed relations then petitioned the Irish Parliament to redress this grievance by transferring to them the moneys designed by Andrews for the Observatory. It would not be right, they contended, that the kindly intentions of the late Provost towards his kindred should be frustrated for the sake of maintaining what they described as "a purely ornamental institution." The authorities of the College protested against this claim. Counsel were heard, and a Committee of the House made a report declaring the situation of the relations to be a hard one. Accordingly, a compromise was made, and the dispute terminated.

The selection of a site for the new astronomical Observatory was made by the Board of Trinity College. The beautiful neighbourhood of Dublin offered a choice of excellent localities. On the north side of the Liffey an Observatory could have been admirably placed, either on the remarkable promontory of Howth or on the elevation of which Dunsink is the summit. On the south side of Dublin there are several eminences that would have been suitable: the breezy heaths at Foxrock combine all necessary conditions; the obelisk hill at Killiney would have given one of the most picturesque sites for an Observatory in the world; while near Delgany two or three other good situations could be mentioned. But the Board of those pre-railway days was naturally guided by the question of proximity. Dunsink was accordingly chosen as the most suitable site within the distance of a reasonable walk from Trinity College.

The northern boundary of the Phoenix Park approaches the little river Tolka, which winds through a succession of delightful bits of sylvan scenery, such as may be found in the wide demesne of Abbotstown and the classic shades of Glasnevin. From the banks of the Tolka, on the opposite side of the park, the pastures ascend in a gentle slope to culminate at Dunsink, where at a distance of half a mile from the stream, of four miles from Dublin, and at a height of 300 feet above the sea, now stands the Observatory. From the commanding position of Dunsink a magnificent view is obtained. To the east the sea is visible, while the southern prospect over the valley of the Liffey is bounded by a range of hills and mountains extending from Killiney to Bray Head, thence to the little Sugar Loaf, the Two Rock and the Three Rock Mountains, over the flank of which the summit of the Great Sugar Loaf is just perceptible. Directly in front opens the fine valley of Glenasmole, with Kippure Mountain, while the range can be followed to its western extremity at Lyons. The climate of Dunsink is well suited for astronomical observation. No doubt here, as elsewhere in Ireland, clouds are abundant, but mists or haze are comparatively unusual, and fogs are almost unknown.

The legal formalities to be observed in assuming occupation exacted a delay of many months; accordingly, it was not until the 10th December, 1782, that a contract could be made with Mr. Graham Moyers for the erection of a meridian-room and a dome for an equatorial, in conjunction with a becoming residence for the astronomer. Before the work was commenced at Dunsink, the Board thought it expedient to appoint the first Professor of Astronomy. They met for this purpose on the 22nd January, 1783, and chose the Rev. Henry Ussher, a Senior Fellow of Trinity College, Dublin. The wisdom of the appointment was immediately shown by the assiduity with which Ussher engaged in founding the observatory. In three years he had erected the buildings and equipped them with instruments, several of which were of his own invention. On the 19th of February, 1785, a special grant of 200 pounds was made by the Board to Dr. Ussher as some recompense for his labours. It happened that the observatory was not the only scientific institution which came into being in Ireland at this period; the newly-kindled ardour for the pursuit of knowledge led, at the same time, to the foundation of the Royal Irish Academy. By a fitting coincidence, the first memoir published in the "Transactions Of The Royal Irish Academy," was by the first Andrews, Professor of Astronomy. It was read on the 13th of June, 1785, and bore the title, "Account of the Observatory belonging to Trinity College," by the Rev. H. Ussher, D.D., M.R.I.A., F.R.S. This communication shows the extensive design that had been originally intended for Dunsink, only a part of which was, however, carried out. For instance, two long corridors, running north and south from the central edifice, which are figured in the paper, never developed into bricks and mortar. We are not told why the original scheme had to be contracted; but perhaps the reason may be not unconnected with a remark of Ussher's, that the College had already advanced from its own funds a sum considerably exceeding the original bequest. The picture of the building shows also the dome for the South equatorial, which was erected many years later.

Ussher died in 1790. During his brief career at the observatory, he observed eclipses, and is stated to have done other scientific work. The minutes of the Board declare that the infant institution had already obtained celebrity by his labours, and they urge the claims of his widow to a pension, on the ground that the disease from which he died had been contracted by his nightly vigils. The Board also promised a grant of fifty guineas as a help to bring out Dr. Ussher's sermons. They advanced twenty guineas to his widow towards the publication of his astronomical papers. They ordered his bust to be executed for the observatory, and offered "The Death of Ussher" as the subject of a prize essay; but, so far as I can find, neither the sermons nor the papers, neither the bust nor the prize essay, ever came into being.

There was keen competition for the chair of Astronomy which the death of Ussher vacated. The two candidates were Rev. John Brinkley, of Caius College, Cambridge, a Senior Wrangler (born at Woodbridge, Suffolk, in 1763), and Mr. Stack, Fellow of Trinity College, Dublin, and author of a book on Optics. A majority of the Board at first supported Stack, while Provost Hely Hutchinson and one or two others supported Brinkley. In those days the Provost had a veto at elections, so that ultimately Stack was withdrawn and Brinkley was elected. This took place on the 11th December, 1790. The national press of the day commented on the preference shown to the young Englishman, Brinkley, over his Irish rival. An animated controversy ensued. The Provost himself condescended to enter the lists and to vindicate his policy by a long letter in the "Public Register" or "Freeman's Journal," of 21st December, 1790. This letter was anonymous, but its authorship is obvious. It gives the correspondence with Maskelyne and other eminent astronomers, whose advice and guidance had been sought by the Provost. It also contends that "the transactions of the Board ought not to be canvassed in the newspapers." For this reference, as well as for much other information, I am indebted to my friend, the Rev. John Stubbs, D.D.

The next event in the history of the Observatory was the issue of Letters Patent (32 Geo. III., A.D. 1792), in which it is recited that "We grant and ordain that there shall be forever hereafter a Professor of Astronomy, on the foundation of Dr. Andrews, to be called and known by the name of the Royal Astronomer of Ireland." The letters pre-

The Observatory, Dunsink

scribe the various duties of the astronomer and the mode of his election. They lay down regulations as to the conduct of the astronomical work, and as to the choice of an assistant. They direct that the Provost and the Senior Fellows shall make a thorough inspection of the observatory once every year in June or July; and this duty was first undertaken on the 5th of July, 1792. It may be noted that the date on which the celebration of the tercentenary of the University was held happens to coincide with the centenary of the first visitation of the observatory. The visitors on the first occasion were A. Murray, Matthew Young, George Hall, and John Barrett. They record that they find the buildings, books and instruments in good condition; but the chief feature in this report, as well as in many which followed it, related to a circumstance to which we have not yet referred.

In the original equipment of the observatory, Ussher, with the natural ambition of a founder, desired to place in it a telescope of more magnificent proportions than could be found anywhere else. The Board gave a spirited support to this enterprise, and negotiations were entered into with the most eminent instrument-maker of those days. This was Jesse Ramsden (1735-1800), famous as the improver of the sextant, as the constructor of the great theodolite used by General Roy in the English Survey, and as the inventor of the dividing engine for graduating astronomical instruments. Ramsden had built for Sir George Schuckburgh the largest and most perfect equatorial ever attempted. He had constructed mural quadrants for Padua and Verona, which elicited the wonder of astronomers when Dr. Maskelyne declared he could detect no error in their graduation so large as two seconds and a half. But Ramsden maintained that even better results would be obtained by superseding the entire quadrant by the circle. He obtained the means of testing this prediction when he completed a superb circle for Palermo of five feet diameter. Finding his anticipations were realised, he desired to apply the same principles on a still grander scale. Ramsden was in this mood when he met with Dr. Ussher. The enthusiasm of the astronomer and the instrument-maker communicated itself to the Board, and a tremendous circle, to be ten feet in diameter, was forthwith projected.

Projected, but never carried out. After Ramsden had to some extent completed a 10-foot circle, he found such difficulties that he tried

a 9-foot, and this again he discarded for an 8-foot, which was ultimately accomplished, though not entirely by himself. Notwithstanding the contraction from the vast proportions originally designed, the
completed instrument must still be regarded as a colossal piece of astronomical workmanship. Even at this day I do not know that any
other observatory can show a circle eight feet in diameter graduated all
round.

I think it is Professor Piazzi Smith who tells us how grateful he was
to find a large telescope he had ordered finished by the opticians on the
very day they had promised it. The day was perfectly correct; it was
only the year that was wrong. A somewhat remarkable experience in
this direction is chronicled by the early reports of the visitors to Dunsink Observatory. I cannot find the date on which the great circle was
ordered from Ramsden, but it is fixed with sufficient precision by an
allusion in Ussher's paper to the Royal Irish Academy, which shows
that by the 13th June, 1785, the order had been given, but that the
abandonment of the 10-foot scale had not then been contemplated. It
was reasonable that the board should allow Ramsden ample time for
the completion of a work at once so elaborate and so novel. It could
not have been finished in a year, nor would there have been much reason for complaint if the maker had found he required two or even
three years more.

Seven years gone, and still no telescope, was the condition in which
the Board found matters at their first visitation in 1792. They had,
however, assurances from Ramsden that the instrument would be
completed within the year; but, alas for such promises, another seven
years rolled on, and in 1799 the place for the great circle was still vacant
at Dunsink. Ramsden had fallen into bad health, and the Board con-
siderately directed that "inquiries should be made." Next year there
was still no progress, so the Board were roused to threaten Ramsden
with a suit at law; but the menace was never executed, for the malady
of the great optician grew worse, and he died that year.

Affairs had now assumed a critical aspect, for the college had advanced much money to Ramsden during these fifteen years, and the
instrument was still unfinished. An appeal was made by the Provost to
Dr. Maskelyne, the Astronomer Royal of England, for his advice and
kindly offices in this emergency. Maskelyne responds—in terms calcu-

lated to allay the anxiety of the Bursar—"Mr. Ramsden has left property behind him, and the College can be in no danger of losing both
their money and the instrument." The business of Ramsden was then
undertaken by Berge, who proceeded to finish the circle quite as deliberately as his predecessor. After four years Berge promised the instrument in the following August, but it did not come. Two years later
(1806) the professor complains that he can get no answer from Berge.
In 1807, it is stated that Berge will send the telescope in a month. He
did not; but in the next year (1808), about twenty-three years after the
great circle was ordered, it was erected at Dunsink, where it is still to be
seen.

The following circumstances have been authenticated by the signa-
tures of Provosts, Proctors, Bursars, and other College dignitaries:—In
1793 the Board ordered two of the clocks at the observatory to be sent
to Mr. Crosthwaite for repairs. Seven years later, in 1800, Mr. Crosthwaite was asked if the clocks were ready. This impatience was clearly
unreasonable, for even in four more years, 1804, we find the two clocks
were still in hand. Two years later, in 1806, the Board determined to
take vigorous action by asking the Bursar to call upon Crosthwaite.
This evidently produced some effect, for in the following year, 1807,
the Professor had no doubt that the clocks would be speedily returned.
After eight years more, in 1815, one of the clocks was still being re-
paired, and so it was in 1816, which is the last record we have of these
interesting time-pieces. Astronomers are, however, accustomed to deal
with such stupendous periods in their calculations, that even the time
taken to repair a clock seems but small in comparison.

The long tenure of the chair of Astronomy by Brinkley is divided
into two nearly equal periods by the year in which the great circle was
erected. Brinkley was eighteen years waiting for his telescope, and he
had eighteen years more in which to use it. During the first of these
periods Brinkley devoted himself to mathematical research; during the
latter he became a celebrated astronomer. Brinkley's mathematical
labours procured for their author some reputation as a mathematician.
They appear to be works of considerable mathematical elegance, but
not indicating any great power of original thought. Perhaps it has been
prejudicial to Brinkley's fame in this direction, that he was immedi-

ately followed in his chair by so mighty a genius as William Rowan Hamilton.

After the great circle had been at last erected, Brinkley was able to begin his astronomical work in earnest. Nor was there much time to lose. He was already forty-five years old, a year older than was Herschel when he commenced his immortal career at Slough. Stimulated by the consciousness of having the command of an instrument of unique perfection, Brinkley loftily attempted the very highest class of astronomical research. He resolved to measure anew with his own eye and with his own hand the constants of aberration and of nutation. He also strove to solve that great problem of the universe, the discovery of the distance of a fixed star.

These were noble problems, and they were nobly attacked. But to appraise with justice this work of Brinkley, done seventy years ago, we must not apply to it the same criterion as we would think right to apply to similar work were it done now. We do not any longer use Brinkley's constant of aberration, nor do we now think that Brinkley's determinations of the star distances were reliable. But, nevertheless, his investigations exercised a marked influence on the progress of science; they stimulated the study of the principles on which exact measurements were to be conducted.

Brinkley had another profession in addition to that of an astronomer. He was a divine. When a man endeavours to pursue two distinct occupations concurrently, it will be equally easy to explain why his career should be successful, or why it should be the reverse. If he succeeds, he will, of course, exemplify the wisdom of having two strings to his bow. Should he fail, it is, of course, because he has attempted to sit on two stools at once. In Brinkley's case, his two professions must be likened to the two strings rather than to the two stools. It is true that his practical experience of his clerical life was very slender. He had made no attempt to combine the routine of a parish with his labours in the observatory. Nor do we associate a special eminence in any department of religious work with his name. If, however, we are to measure Brinkley's merits as a divine by the ecclesiastical preferment which he received, his services to theology must have rivalled his services to astronomy. Having been raised step by step in the Church, he was at last appointed to the See of Cloyne, in 1826, as the successor of Bishop Berkeley.

Now, though it was permissible for the Archdeacon to be also the Andrews Professor, yet when the Archdeacon became a Bishop, it was understood that he should transfer his residence from the observatory to the palace. The chair of Astronomy accordingly became vacant. Brinkley's subsequent career seems to have been devoted entirely to ecclesiastical matters, and for the last ten years of his life he did not contribute a paper to any scientific society. Arago, after a characteristic lament that Brinkley should have forsaken the pursuit of science for the temporal and spiritual attractions of a bishopric, pays a tribute to the conscientiousness of the quondam astronomer, who would not even allow a telescope to be brought into the palace lest his mind should be distracted from his sacred duties.

The good bishop died on the 13th September, 1835. He was buried in the chapel of Trinity College, and a fine monument to his memory is a familiar object at the foot of the noble old staircase of the library. The best memorial of Brinkley is his admirable book on the "Elements of Plane Astronomy." It passed through many editions in his lifetime, and even at the present day the same work, revised first by Dr. Luby, and more recently by the Rev. Dr. Stubbs and Dr. Brunnow, has a large and well-merited circulation.

JOHN HERSCHEL.

This illustrious son of an illustrious father was born at Slough, near Windsor, on the 7th March, 1792. He was the only child of Sir William Herschel, who had married somewhat late in life, as we have already mentioned.

The surroundings among which the young astronomer was reared afforded him an excellent training for that career on which he was to enter, and in which he was destined to attain a fame only less brilliant than that of his father. The circumstances of his youth permitted him to enjoy one great advantage which was denied to the elder Herschel. He was able, from his childhood, to devote himself almost exclusively to intellectual pursuits. William Herschel, in the early part of his career, had only been able to snatch occasional hours for study from his busy life as a professional musician. But the son, having been born with a taste for the student's life, was fortunate enough to have been endowed with the leisure and the means to enjoy it from the commencement. His early years have been so well described by the late Professor Pritchard in the "Report of the Council of the Royal Astronomical Society for 1872," that I venture to make an extract here:—

"A few traits of John Herschel's boyhood, mentioned by himself in his maturer life, have been treasured up by those who were dear to him, and the record of some of them may satisfy a curiosity as pardonable as inevitable, which craves to learn through what early steps great men or great nations become illustrious. His home was singular, and singularly calculated to nurture into greatness any child born as John Herschel was with natural gifts, capable of wide development. At the head of the house there was the aged, observant, reticent philosopher, and rarely far away his devoted sister, Caroline Herschel, whose labours and whose fame are still cognisable as a beneficent satellite to the brighter light of her illustrious brother. It was in the companionship of these remarkable persons, and under the shadow of his father's wonderful telescope, that John Herschel passed his boyish years. He saw them, in silent but ceaseless industry, busied about things which had no apparent concern with the world outside the walls of that well-known house, but which, at a later period of his life, he, with an unrivalled eloquence, taught his countrymen to appreciate as foremost among those living influences which but satisfy and elevate the noblest instincts of our nature. What sort of intercourse passed between the father and the boy may be gathered from an incident or two which he narrated as having impressed themselves permanently on the memory of his youth. He once asked his father what he thought was the oldest of all things. The father replied, after the Socratic method, by putting another question: 'And what do you yourself suppose is the oldest of all things?' The boy was not successful in his answers, thereon the old astronomer took up a small stone from the garden walk: 'There, my child, there is the oldest of all the things that I certainly know.' On another occasion his father is said to have asked the boy, 'What sort of things, do you think, are most alike?' The delicate, blue-eyed boy, after a short pause, replied, 'The leaves of the same tree are most like each other.' 'Gather, then, a handful of leaves of that tree,' rejoined the philosopher, 'and choose two that are alike.' The boy failed; but he hid the lesson in his heart, and his thoughts were revealed after many days. These incidents may be trifles; nor should we record them here had not John Herschel himself, though singularly reticent about his personal emotions, recorded them as having made a strong impression on his mind. Beyond all doubt we can trace therein, first, that grasp and grouping of many things in one, implied in the stone as the oldest of things; and, secondly, that fine and subtle discrimination of each thing out of many like things as forming the main features which characterized the habit of our venerated friend's philosophy."

John Herschel entered St. John's College, Cambridge, when he was seventeen years of age. His university career abundantly fulfilled his father's eager desire, that his only son should develop a capacity for the pursuit of science. After obtaining many lesser distinctions, he finally

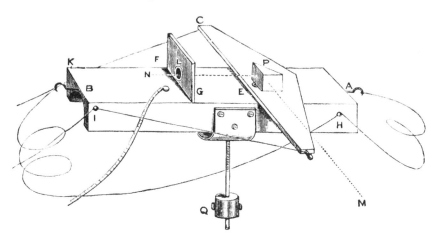

ASTRONOMETER MADE BY SIR J. HERSCHEL TO COMPARE THE LIGHT OF
CERTAIN STARS BY INTERVENTION OF THE MOON.

came out as Senior Wrangler in 1813. It was, indeed, a notable year in the mathematical annals of the University. Second on that list, in which Herschel's name was first, appeared that of the illustrious Peacock, afterwards Dean of Ely, who remained throughout life one of Herschel's most intimate friends.

Almost immediately after taking his degree, Herschel gave evidence of possessing a special aptitude for original scientific investigation. He sent to the Royal Society a mathematical paper which was published in the *Philosophical Transactions*. Doubtless the splendour that attached to the name he bore assisted him in procuring early recognition of his own great powers. Certain it is that he was made a Fellow of the Royal Society at the unprecedentedly early age of twenty-one. Even after this remarkable encouragement to adopt a scientific career as the business of his life, it does not seem that John Herschel at first contemplated devoting himself exclusively to science. He commenced to prepare for the profession of the Law by entering as a student at the Middle Temple, and reading with a practising barrister.

But a lawyer John Herschel was not destined to become. Circumstances brought him into association with some leading scientific men. He presently discovered that his inclinations tended more and more in the direction of purely scientific pursuits. Thus it came to pass that the original intention as to the calling which he should follow was gradually abandoned. Fortunately for science Herschel found its pursuit so attractive that he was led, as his father had been before him, to give up his whole life to the advancement of knowledge. Nor was it unnatural that a Senior Wrangler, who had once tasted the delights of mathematical research, should have been tempted to devote much time to this fascinating pursuit. By the time John Herschel was twenty-nine he had published so much mathematical work, and his researches were considered to possess so much merit, that the Royal Society awarded him the Copley Medal, which was the highest distinction it was capable of conferring.

At the death of his father in 1822, John Herschel, with his tastes already formed for a scientific career, found himself in the possession of ample means. To him also passed all his father's great telescopes and apparatus. These material aids, together with a dutiful sense of filial obligation, decided him to make practical astronomy the main work of his life. He decided to continue to its completion that great survey of the heavens which had already been inaugurated, and, indeed, to a large extent accomplished, by his father.

The first systematic piece of practical astronomical work which John Herschel undertook was connected with the measurement of what are known as "Double Stars." It should be observed, that there are in the heavens a number of instances in which two stars are seen in very close association. In the case of those objects to which the expression "Double Stars" is generally applied, the two luminous points are so close together that even though they might each be quite bright enough to be visible to the unaided eye, yet their proximity is such that they cannot be distinguished as two separate objects without optical aid. The two stars seem fused together into one. In the telescope, however, the bodies may be discerned separately, though they are frequently so close together that it taxes the utmost power of the instrument to indicate the division between them.

The appearance presented by a double star might arise from the circumstance that the two stars, though really separated from each other by prodigious distances, happened to lie nearly in the same line of vision, as seen from our point of view. No doubt, many of the so-called double stars could be accounted for on this supposition. Indeed, in the early days when but few double stars were known, and when tele-

SIR JOHN HERSCHEL.

scopes were not powerful enough to exhibit the numerous close doubles which have since been brought to light, there seems to have been a tendency to regard all double stars as merely such perspective effects. It was not at first suggested that there could be any physical connection between the components of each pair. The appearance presented was regarded as merely due to the circumstance that the line joining the two bodies happened to pass near the earth.

In the early part of his career, Sir William Herschel seems to have entertained the view then generally held by other astronomers with regard to the nature of these stellar pairs. The great observer thought that the double stars could therefore be made to afford a means of solving that problem in which so many of the observers of the skies had been engaged, namely, the determination of the distances of the stars from the earth. Herschel saw that the displacement of the earth in its annual movement round the sun would produce an apparent shift in the place of the nearer of the two stars relatively to the other, supposed to be much more remote. If this shift could be measured, then the distance of the nearer of the stars could be estimated with some degree of precision.

As has not unfrequently happened in the history of science, an effect was perceived of a very different nature from that which had been anticipated. If the relative places of the two stars had been apparently deranged merely in consequence of the motion of the earth, then the phenomenon would be an annual one. After the lapse of a year the two stars would have regained their original relative positions. This was the effect for which William Herschel was looking. In certain of the so called double stars, he, no doubt, did find a movement. He detected the remarkable fact that both the apparent distance and the relative positions of the two bodies were changing. But what was his surprise to observe that these alterations were not of an annually periodic character. It became evident then that in some cases one of the component stars was actually revolving around the other, in an orbit which required many years for its completion. Here was indeed a remarkable discovery. It was clearly impossible to suppose that movements of this kind could be mere apparent displacements, arising from the annual shift in our point of view, in consequence of the revolution of the earth. Herschel's discovery established the interesting fact that, in certain of these double stars, or binary stars, as these particular objects are more expressively designated, there is an actual orbital revolution of a character similar to that which the earth performs around the sun. Thus it was demonstrated that in these particular double stars the nearness of the two components was not merely apparent. The objects must actually lie close together at a distance which is small in comparison with the distance at which either of them is separated from the earth. The fact that the heavens contain pairs of twin suns in mutual revolution was thus brought to light.

In consequence of this beautiful discovery, the attention of astronomers was directed to the subject of double stars with a degree of interest which these objects had never before excited. It was therefore not unnatural that John Herschel should have been attracted to this branch of astronomical work. Admiration for his father's discovery alone might have suggested that the son should strive to develop this territory newly opened up to research. But it also happened that the mathematical talents of the younger Herschel inclined his inquiries in the same direction. He saw clearly that, when sufficient observations of any particular binary star had been accumulated, it would then be within the power of the mathematician to elicit from those observations the shape and the

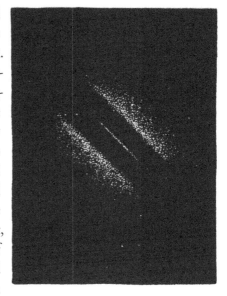

NEBULA IN SOUTHERN HEMISPHERE, DRAWN BY SIR JOHN HERSCHEL.

position in space of the path which each of the revolving stars described around the other. Indeed, in some cases he would be able to perform the astonishing feat of determining from his calculations the weight of these distant suns, and thus be enabled to compare them with the mass of our own sun.

But this work must follow the observations, it could not precede them. The first step was therefore to observe and to measure with the utmost care the positions and distances of those particular double stars which appear to offer the greatest promise in this particular research. In 1821, Herschel and a friend of his, Mr. James South, agreed to work together with this object. South was a medical man with an ardent devotion to science, and possessed of considerable wealth. He procured the best astronomical instruments that money could obtain, and became a most enthusiastic astronomer and a practical observer of tremendous energy.

South and John Herschel worked together for two years in the observation and measurement of the double stars discovered by Sir William Herschel. In the course of this time their assiduity was rewarded by the accumulation of so great a mass of careful measurements that when published, they formed quite a volume in the "Philo-sophical Transactions." The value and accuracy of the work, when es-timated by standards which form proper criteria for that period, is universally recognised. It greatly promoted the progress of sidereal as-tronomy, and the authors were in consequence awarded medals from the Royal Society, and the Royal Astronomical Society, as well as simi-lar testimonials from various foreign institutions.

This work must, however, be regarded as merely introductory to the main labours of John Herschel's life. His father devoted the greater part of his years as an observer to what he called his "sweeps" of the heavens. The great reflecting telescope, twenty feet long, was moved slowly up and down through an arc of about two degrees towards and from the pole, while the celestial panorama passed slowly in the course of the diurnal motion before the keenly watching eye of the as-tronomer. Whenever a double star traversed the field Herschel de-scribed it to his sister Caroline, who, as we have already mentioned, was his invariable assistant in his midnight watches. When a nebula ap-peared, then he estimated its size and its brightness, he noticed whether it had a nucleus, or whether it had stars disposed in any sig-nificant manner with regard to it. He also dictated any other circum-stance which he deemed worthy of record. These observations were duly committed to writing by the same faithful and indefatigable scribe, whose business it also was to take a memorandum of the exact position of the object as indicated by a dial placed in front of her desk, and connected with the telescope.

John Herschel undertook the important task of re-observing the various double stars and nebulae which had been discovered during these memorable vigils. The son, however, lacked one inestimable ad-vantage which had been possessed by the father. John Herschel had no assistant to discharge all those duties which Caroline had so efficiently accomplished. He had, therefore, to modify the system of sweeping previously adopted in order to enable all the work both of observing and of recording to be done by himself. This, in many ways, was a great drawback to the work of the younger astronomer. The division of labour between the observer and the scribe enables a greatly increased quantity of work to be got through. It is also distinctly disadvanta-geous to an observer to have to use his eye at the telescope directly after he has been employing it for reading the graduations on a circle, by the light of a lamp, or for entering memoranda in a note book. Nebulae, especially, are often so excessively faint that they can only be properly observed by an eye which is in that highly sensitive condition which is obtained by long continuance in darkness. The frequent withdrawal of the eye from the dark field of the telescope, and the application of it to reading by artificial light, is very prejudicial to its use for the more delicate purpose. John Herschel, no doubt, availed himself of every precaution to mitigate the ill effects of this inconvenience as much as possible, but it must have told upon his labours as compared with those of his father.

But nevertheless John Herschel did great work during his "sweeps." He was specially particular to note all the double stars which presented themselves to his observation. Of course some little discretion must be allowed in deciding as to what degree of proximity in adjacent stars does actually bring them within the category of "double stars." Sir John set down all such objects as seemed to him likely to be of interest, and the results of his discoveries in this branch of astronomy amount to some thousands. Six or seven great memoirs in the *Transactions* of the Royal Astronomical Society have been devoted to giving an account of his labours in this department of astronomy.

One of the achievements by which Sir John Herschel is best known is his invention of a method by which the orbits of binary stars could be determined. It will be observed that when one star revolves around another in consequence of the law of gravitation, the orbit described must be an ellipse. This ellipse, however, generally speaking, appears to us more or less foreshortened, for it is easily seen that only under highly exceptional circumstances would the plane in which the stars move happen to be directly square to the line of view. It therefore follows that what we observe is not exactly the track of one star around the other; it is rather the projection of that track as seen on the surface of the sky. Now it is remarkable that this apparent path is still an ellipse. Herschel contrived a very ingenious and simple method by which he could discover from the observations the size and position of the ellipse in which the revolution actually takes place. He showed how, from the study of the apparent orbit of the star, and from certain measurements which could easily be effected upon it, the determination of

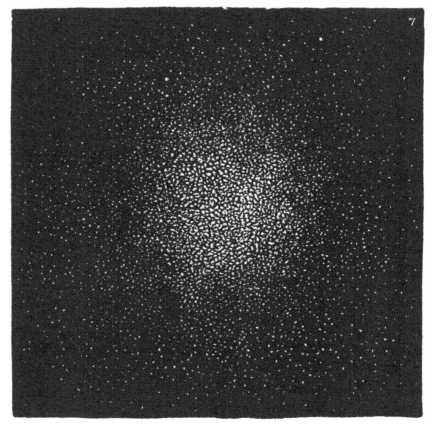

THE CLUSTER IN THE CENTAUR, DRAWN BY SIRE JOHN HERSCHEL.

the true ellipse in which the movement is performed could be arrived at. In other words, Herschel solved in a beautiful manner the problem of finding the true orbits of double stars. The importance of this work may be inferred from the fact that it has served as the basis on which scores of other investigators have studied the fascinating subject of the movement of binary stars.

The labours, both in the discovery and measurement of the double stars, and in the discussion of the observations with the object of finding the orbits of such stars as are in actual revolution, received due recognition in yet another gold medal awarded by the Royal Society. An address was delivered on the occasion by the Duke of Sussex (30th November, 1833), in the course of which, after stating that the medal had been conferred on Sir John Herschel, he remarks:—

"It has been said that distance of place confers the same privilege as distance of time, and I should gladly avail myself of the privilege which is thus afforded me by Sir John Herschel's separation from his country and friends, to express my admiration of his character in stronger terms than I should otherwise venture to use; for the language of panegyric, however sincerely it may flow from the heart, might be mistaken for that of flattery, if it could not thus claim somewhat of an historical character; but his great attainments in almost every department of human knowledge, his fine powers as a philosophical writer, his great services and his distinguished devotion to science, the high principles which have regulated his conduct in every relation of life, and, above all, his engaging modesty, which is the crown of all his other virtues, presenting such a model of an accomplished philosopher as can rarely be found beyond the regions of fiction, demand abler pens than mine to describe them in adequate terms, however much inclined I might feel to undertake the task."

The first few lines of the eulogium just quoted allude to Herschel's absence from England. This was not merely an episode of interest in the career of Herschel, it was the occasion of one of the greatest scientific expeditions in the whole history of astronomy.

Herschel had, as we have seen, undertaken a revision of his father's "sweeps" for new objects, in those skies which are visible from our latitudes in the northern hemisphere. He had well-nigh completed this task. Zone by zone the whole of the heavens which could be observed from Windsor had passed under his review. He had added hundreds to the list of nebulae discovered by his father. He had announced thousands of double stars. At last, however, the great survey was accomplished. The contents of the northern hemisphere, so far at least as they could be disclosed by his telescope of twenty feet focal length, had been revealed.

But Herschel felt that this mighty task had to be supplemented by another of almost equal proportions, before it could be said that the twenty-foot telescope had done its work. It was only the northern half of the celestial sphere which had been fully explored. The southern half was almost virgin territory, for no other astronomer was possessed of a telescope of such power as those which the Herschels had used. It is true, of course, that as a certain margin of the southern hemisphere

SIR JOHN HERSCHEL'S OBSERVATORY AT FELHAUSEN, CAPE OF
GOOD HOPE.

was visible from these latitudes, it had been more or less scrutinized by
observers in northern skies. And the glimpses which had thus been obtained of the celestial objects in the southern sky, were such as to make
an eager astronomer long for a closer acquaintance with the celestial
wonders of the south. The most glorious object in the sidereal heavens,
the Great Nebula in Orion, lies indeed in that southern hemisphere to
which the younger Herschel's attention now became directed. It fortunately happens, however, for votaries of astronomy all the world over,
that Nature has kindly placed her most astounding object, the great
Nebula in Orion, in such a favoured position, near the equator, that
from a considerable range of latitudes, both north and south, the wonders of the Nebula can be explored. There are grounds for thinking
that the southern heavens contain noteworthy objects which, on the
whole, are nearer to the solar system than are the noteworthy objects in
the northern skies. The nearest star whose distance is known, Alpha

Centauri, lies in the southern hemisphere, and so also does the most splendid cluster of stars.

Influenced by the desire to examine these objects, Sir John Herschel determined to take his great telescope to a station in the southern hemisphere, and thus complete his survey of the sidereal heavens. The latitude of the Cape of Good Hope is such that a suitable site could be there found for his purpose. The purity of the skies in South Africa promised to provide for the astronomer those clear nights which his delicate task of surveying the nebulae would require.

On November 13, 1833, Sir John Herschel, who had by this time received the honour of knighthood from William IV., sailed from Portsmouth for the Cape of Good Hope, taking with him his gigantic instruments. After a voyage of two months, which was considered to be a fair passage in those days, he landed in Table Bay, and having duly reconnoitred various localities, he decided to place his observatory at a place called Feldhausen, about six miles from Cape Town, near the base of the Table Mountain. A commodious residence was there available, and in it he settled with his family. A temporary building was erected to contain the equatorial, but the great twenty-foot telescope was accommodated with no more shelter than is provided by the open canopy of heaven.

As in his earlier researches at home, the attention of the great astronomer at the Cape of Good Hope was chiefly directed to the measurement of the relative positions and distances apart of the double stars, and to the close examination of the nebulae. In the delineation of the form of these latter objects Herschel found ample employment for his skilful pencil. Many of the drawings he has made of the celestial wonders in the southern sky are admirable examples of celestial portraiture.

The number of the nebulae and of those kindred objects, the star clusters, which Herschel studied in the southern heavens, during four years of delightful labour, amount in all to one thousand seven hundred and seven. His notes on their appearance, and the determinations of their positions, as well as his measurements of double stars, and much other valuable astronomical research, were published in a splendid volume, brought out at the cost of the Duke of Northumberland.

GRANITE COLUMN AT FELDHUASEN, CAPE TOWN, TO COMMEMORATE
SIR JOHN HERSHEL'S SURVEY AT THE SOUTHERN HEAVENS.

This is, indeed, a monumental work, full of interesting and instructive reading for any one who has a taste for astronomy.

Herschel had the good fortune to be at the Cape on the occasion of the periodical return of Halley's great comet in 1833. To the study of this body he gave assiduous attention, and the records of his observations form one of the most interesting chapters in that remarkable volume to which we have just referred.

Early in 1838 Sir John Herschel returned to England. He had made many friends at the Cape, who deeply sympathised with his self- imposed labours while he was resident among them. They desired to preserve the recollection of this visit, which would always, they considered, be a source of gratification in the colony. Accordingly, a number of scientific friends in that part of the world raised a monument with a suitable inscription, on the spot which had been occupied by the great twenty-foot reflector at Feldhausen.

His return to England after five years of absence was naturally an occasion for much rejoicing among the lovers of astronomy. He was entertained at a memorable banquet, and the Queen, at her corona-tion, made him a baronet. His famous aunt Caroline, at that time aged eighty, was still in the enjoyment of her faculties, and was able to estimate at its true value the further lustre which was added to the name she bore. But there is reason to believe that her satisfaction was not quite unmixed with other feelings. With whatever favour she might regard her nephew, he was still not the brother to whom her life had been devoted. So jealous was this vigorous old lady of the fame of the great brother William, that she could hardly hear with patience of the achievements of any other astronomer, and this failing existed in some degree even when that other astronomer happened to be her illustrious nephew.

With Sir John Herschel's survey of the Southern Hemisphere it may be said that his career as an observing astronomer came to a close. He did not again engage in any systematic telescopic research. But it must not be inferred from this statement that he desisted from active astronomical work. It has been well observed that Sir John Herschel was perhaps the only astronomer who has studied with success, and advanced by original research, every department of the great science with which his name is associated. It was to some other branches of astronomy besides those concerned with looking through telescopes, that the rest of the astronomer's life was to be devoted.

To the general student Sir John Herschel is best known by the volume which he published under the title of "Outlines of Astronomy." This is, indeed, a masterly work, in which the characteristic difficulties of the subject are resolutely faced and expounded with as much simplicity as their nature will admit. As a literary effort this work is admirable, both on account of its picturesque language and the ennobling conceptions of the universe which it unfolds. The student who desires to become acquainted with those recondite departments of astronomy, in which the effects of the disturbing action of one planet upon the motions of another planet are considered, will turn to the chapters in Herschel's famous work on the subject. There he will find this complex matter elucidated, without resort to difficult mathematics. Edition after edition of this valuable work has appeared, and though the advances of modern astronomy have left it somewhat out of date in certain departments, yet the expositions it contains of the fundamental parts of the science still remain unrivalled.

Another great work which Sir John undertook after his return from the Cape, was a natural climax to those labours on which his father and he had been occupied for so many years. We have already explained how the work of both these observers had been mainly devoted to the study of the nebulae and the star clusters. The results of their discoveries had been announced to the world in numerous isolated memoirs. The disjointed nature of these publications made their use very inconvenient. But still it was necessary for those who desired to study the marvellous objects discovered by the Herschels, to have frequent recourse to the original works. To incorporate all the several observations of nebular into one great systematic catalogue, seemed, therefore, to be an indispensable condition of progress in this branch of knowledge. No one could have been so fitted for this task as Sir John Herschel. He, therefore, attacked and carried through the great undertaking. Thus at last a grand catalogue of nebulae and clusters was produced. Never before was there so majestic an inventory. If we remember that each of the nebulae is an object so vast, that the whole of the solar system would form an inconsiderable speck by comparison, what are we to think of a collection in which these objects are enumerated in thousands? In this great catalogue we find arranged in systematic order all the nebulae and all the clusters which had been revealed by the diligence of the Herschels, father and son, in the Northern Hemisphere, and of the son alone in the Southern Hemisphere. Nor should we omit to mention that the labours of other astronomers were likewise incorporated. It was unavoidable that the descriptions given to each of the objects should be very slight. Abbreviations are used, which indicate that a nebula is bright, or very bright, or extremely bright, or faint, or very faint, or extremely faint. Such phrases have certainly but a relative and technical meaning in such a catalogue. The nebulae entered as extremely bright by the experienced astronomer are only so described by way of contrast to the great majority of these delicate telescopic objects. Most of the nebulae, indeed, are so difficult to see, that they admit of but very slight description. It should be observed that Herschel's catalogue augmented the number of known nebulous objects to more than ten times that collected into any catalogue which had ever been compiled before the days of William Herschel's observing began. But the study of these objects still advances, and the great telescopes now in use could probably show at least twice as many of these objects as are contained in the list of Herschel, of which a new and enlarged edition has since been brought out by Dr. Dreyer.

One of the best illustrations of Sir John Herschel's literary powers is to be found in the address which he delivered at the Royal Astronomical Society, on the occasion of presenting a medal to Mr. Francis Baily, in recognition of his catalogue of stars. The passage I shall here cite places in its proper aspect the true merit of the laborious duty involved in such a task as that which Mr. Baily had carried through with such success:—

"If we ask to what end magnificent establishments are maintained by states and sovereigns, furnished with masterpieces of art, and placed under the direction of men of first-rate talent and high-minded enthusiasm, sought out for those qualities among the foremost in the ranks of science, if we demand QUI BONO? for what good a Bradley has toiled, or a Maskelyne or a Piazzi has worn out his venerable age in watching, the answer is—not to settle mere speculative points in the doctrine of the universe; not to cater for the pride of man by refined inquiries into the remoter mysteries of nature; not to trace the path of our system through space, or its history through past and future eternities. These, indeed, are noble ends and which I am far from any thought of depreciating; the mind swells in their contemplation, and attains in their pursuit an expansion and a hardihood which fit it for the boldest enterprise. But the direct practical utility of such labours is fully worthy of their speculative grandeur. The stars are the landmarks of the universe; and, amidst the endless and complicated fluctuations of our system, seem placed by its Creator as guides and records, not merely to elevate our minds by the contemplation of what is vast, but to teach us to direct our actions by reference to what is immutable in His works. It is, indeed, hardly possible to over-appreciate their value in this point of view. Every well-determined star, from the moment its place is registered, becomes to the astronomer, the geographer, the navigator, the surveyor, a point of departure which can never deceive or fail him, the same for ever and in all places, of a delicacy so extreme as to be a test for every instrument yet invented by man, yet equally adapted for the most ordinary purposes; as available for regulating a town clock as for conducting a navy to the Indies; as effective for map-

ping down the intricacies of a petty barony as for adjusting the boundaries of Transatlantic empires. When once its place has been thoroughly ascertained and carefully recorded, the brazen circle with
which that useful work was done may moulder, the marble pillar may
totter on its base, and the astronomer himself survive only in the gratitude of posterity; but the record remains, and transfuses all its own ex-
actness into every determination which takes it for a groundwork,
giving to inferior instruments—nay, even to temporary contrivances,
and to the observations of a few weeks or days—all the precision attained originally at the cost of so much time, labour, and expense."

Sir John Herschel wrote many other works besides those we have
mentioned. His "Treatise on Meteorology" is, indeed, a standard work
on this subject, and numerous articles from the same pen on miscella-
neous subjects, which have been collected and reprinted, seemed as a
relaxation from his severe scientific studies. Like certain other great
mathematicians Herschel was also a poet, and he published a translation of the Iliad into blank verse.

In his later years Sir John Herschel lived a retired life. For a brief period he had, indeed, been induced to accept the office of Master of the
Mint. It was, however, evident that the routine of such an occupation
was not in accordance with his tastes, and he gladly resigned it, to return to the seclusion of his study in his beautiful home at Colling-
wood, in Kent.

His health having gradually failed, he died on the 11th May, 1871,
in the seventy-ninth year of his age.

THE EARL OF ROSSE.

The subject of our present sketch occupies quite a distinct position in scientific history. Unlike many others who have risen by their scientific discoveries from obscurity to fame, the great Earl of Rosse was himself born in the purple. His father, who, under the title of Sir Lawrence Parsons, had occupied a distinguished position in the Irish Parliament, succeeded on the death of his father to the Earldom which had been recently created. The subject of our present memoir was, therefore, the third of the Earls of Rosse, and he was born in York on June 17, 1800. Prior to his father's death in 1841, he was known as Lord Oxmantown.

The University education of the illustrious astronomer was begun in Dublin and completed at Oxford. We do not hear in his case of any very remarkable University career. Lord Rosse was, however, a diligent student, and obtained a first-class in mathematics. He always took a great deal of interest in social questions, and was a profound student of political economy. He had a seat in the House of Commons, as member for King's County, from 1821 to 1834, his ancestral estate being situated in this part of Ireland.

Lord Rosse was endowed by nature with a special taste for mechanical pursuits. Not only had he the qualifications of a scientific engineer, but he had the manual dexterity which qualified him personally to carry out many practical arts. Lord Rosse was, in fact, a skilful mechanic, an experienced founder, and an ingenious optician. His acquaintances were largely among those who were interested in mechanical pursuits, and it was his delight to visit the works or engineering establishments where refined processes in the arts were being carried on. It has often been stated—and as I have been told by mem-

THE EARL OF ROSSE.

bers of his family, truly stated—that on one occasion, after he had been shown over some large works in the north of England, the proprietor bluntly said that he was greatly in want of a foreman, and would indeed be pleased if his visitor, who had evinced such extraordinary capacity for mechanical operations, would accept the post. Lord Rosse produced his card, and gently explained that he was not exactly the right man, but he appreciated the compliment, and this led to a pleasant dinner, and was the basis of a long friendship.

I remember on one occasion hearing Lord Rosse explain how it was

BIRR CASTLE.

that he came to devote his attention to astronomy. It appears that when he found himself in the possession of leisure and of means, he deliberately cast around to think how that means and that leisure could be most usefully employed. Nor was it surprising that he should search for a direction which would offer special scope for his mechanical tastes. He came to the conclusion that the building of great telescopes was an art which had received no substantial advance since the great days of William Herschel. He saw that to construct mighty instruments for studying the heavens required at once the command of time and the command of wealth, while he also felt that this was a subject the inherent difficulties of which would tax to the uttermost whatever mechanical skill he might possess. Thus it was he decided that the construction of great telescopes should become the business of his life.

In the centre of Ireland, seventy miles from Dublin, on the border between King's County and Tipperary, is a little town whereof we must be cautious before writing the name. The inhabitants of that town frequently insist that its name is Birr,˙ while the official designation is Parsonstown, and to this day for every six people who apply one name to the town, there will be half a dozen who use the other. But whichever it may be, Birr or Parsonstown—and I shall generally call it by the latter name—it is a favourite specimen of an Irish county town. The widest street is called the Oxmantown Mall. It is bordered by the dwelling-houses of the chief residents, and adorned with rows

---

˙Considering the fame acquired by Parsonstown from Lord Rosse's mirrors, it may be interesting to note the following extract from "The Natural History of Ireland," by Dr. Gerard Boate, Thomas Molyneux M.D., F.R.S., and others, which shows that 150 years ago Parsonstown was famous for its glass:—

"We shall conclude this chapter with the glass, there having been several glasshouses set up by the English in Ireland, none in Dublin or other cities, but all of them in the country; amongst which the principal was that of Birre, a market town, otherwise called Parsonstown, after one Sir Lawrence Parsons, who, having purchased that lordship, built a goodly house upon it; his son William Parsons having succeeded him in the possession of it; which town is situate in Queen's County, about fifty miles (Irish) to the southwest of Dublin, upon the borders of the two provinces of Leinster and Munster; from this place Dublin was furnished with all sorts of window and drinking glasses, and such other as commonly are in use. One part of the materials, viz., the sand, they had out of England; the other, to wit the ashes, they made in the place of ash-tree, and used no other. The chiefest difficulty was to get the clay for the pots to melt the materials in; this they had out of the north."—Chap. XXI., Sect. VIII. "Of the Glass made in Ireland."

THE MALL, PARSONTOWN.

of stately trees. At one end of this distinctly good feature in the town is the Parish Church, while at the opposite end are the gates leading into Birr Castle, the ancestral home of the house of Parsons. Passing through the gates the visitor enters a spacious demesne, possessing much beauty of wood and water, one of the most pleasing features being the junction of the two rivers, which unite at a spot ornamented by beautiful timber. At various points illustrations of the engineering skill of the great Earl will be observed. The beauty of the park has been greatly enhanced by the construction of an ample lake, designed with the consummate art by which art is concealed. Even in mid-summer it is enlivened by troops of wild ducks preening themselves in that confidence which they enjoy in those happy localities where the sound of a gun is seldom heard. The water is led into the lake by a tube which passes under one of the two rivers just mentioned, while the overflow from the lake turns a water-wheel, which works a pair of elevators ingeniously constructed for draining the low-lying parts of the estate.

Birr Castle itself is a noble mansion with reminiscences from the time of Cromwell. It is surrounded by a moat and a drawbridge of modern construction, and from its windows beautiful views can be had over the varied features of the park. But while the visitors to Parsonstown will look with great interest on this residence of an Irish landlord, whose delight it was to dwell in his own country, and among his own people, yet the feature which they have specially come to observe is not to be found in the castle itself. On an extensive lawn, sweeping down from the moat towards the lake, stand two noble masonry walls. They are turreted and clad with ivy, and considerably loftier than any ordinary house. As the visitor approaches, he will see between those walls what may at first sight appear to him to be the funnel of a steamer lying down horizontally. On closer approach he will find that it is an immense wooden tube, sixty feet long, and upwards of six feet in diameter. It is in fact large enough to admit of a tall man entering into it and walking erect right through from one end to the other. This is indeed the most gigantic instrument which has ever been constructed for the purpose of exploring the heavens. Closely adjoining the walls between which the great tube swings, is a little building called "The Observatory." In this the smaller instruments are contained, and there are kept the books which are necessary for reference.

The observatory also offers shelter to the observers, and provides the bright fire and the cup of warm tea, which are so acceptable in the occasional intervals of a night's observation passed on the top of the walls with no canopy but the winter sky.

Almost the first point which would strike the visitor to Lord Rosse's telescope is that the instrument at which he is looking is not only enormously greater than anything of the kind that he has ever seen before, but also that it is something of a totally different nature. In an ordinary telescope he is accustomed to find a tube with lenses of glass at either end, while the large telescopes that we see in our observatories are also in general constructed on the same principle. At one end there is the object-glass, and at the other end the eye-piece, and of course it is obvious that with an instrument of this construction it is to the lower end of the tube that the eye of the observer must be placed when the telescope is pointed to the skies. But in Lord Rosse's telescope you would look in vain for these glasses, and it is not at the lower end of the instrument that you are to take your station when you are going to make your observations. The astronomer at Parsonstown has rather to avail himself of the ingenious system of staircases and galleries, by which he is enabled to obtain access to the mouth of the great tube. The colossal telescope which swings between the great walls, like Herschel's great telescope already mentioned, is a reflector, the original invention of which is due of course to Newton. The optical work which is accomplished by the lenses in the ordinary telescope is effected in the type of instrument constructed by Lord Rosse by a reflecting mirror which is placed at the lower end of the vast tube. The mirror in this instrument is made of a metal consisting of two parts of copper to one of tin. As we have already seen, this mixture forms an alloy of a very peculiar nature. The copper and the tin both surrender their distinctive qualities, and unite to form a material of a very different physical character. The copper is tough and brown, the tin is no doubt silvery in hue, but soft and almost fibrous in texture. When the two metals are mixed together in the proportions I have stated, the alloy obtained is intensely hard and quite brittle being in both these respects utterly unlike either of the two ingredients of which it is composed. It does, however, resemble the tin in its whiteness, but it acquires a lustre far brighter than tin; in fact, this alloy hardly falls short of silver itself in its brilliance when polished.

The first duty that Lord Rosse had to undertake was the construction of this tremendous mirror, six feet across, and about four or five inches thick. The dimensions were far in excess of those which had been contemplated in any previous attempt of the same kind. Herschel had no doubt fashioned one mirror of four feet in diameter, and many others of smaller dimensions, but the processes which he employed had never been fully published, and it was obvious that, with a large increase in dimensions, great additional difficulties had to be encountered. Difficulties began at the very commencement of the process, and were experienced in one form or another at every subsequent stage. In the first place, the mere casting of a great disc of this mixture of tin and copper, weighing something like three or four tons, involved very troublesome problems. No doubt a casting of this size, if the material had been, for example, iron, would have offered no difficulties beyond those with which every practical founder is well acquainted, and which he has to encounter daily in the course of his ordinary work. But speculum metal is a material of a very intractable description. There is, of course, no practical difficulty in melting the copper, nor in adding the proper proportion of tin when the copper has been melted. There may be no great difficulty in arranging an organization by which several crucibles, filled with the molten material, shall be poured simultaneously so as to obtain the requisite mass of metal, but from this point the difficulties begin. For speculum metal when cold is excessively brittle, and were the casting permitted to cool like an ordinary copper or iron casting, the mirror would inevitably fly into pieces. Lord Rosse, therefore, found it necessary to anneal the casting with extreme care by allowing it to cool very slowly. This was accomplished by drawing the disc of metal as soon as it had entered into the solid state, though still glowing red, into an annealing oven. There the temperature was allowed to subside so gradually, that six weeks elapsed before the mirror had reached the temperature of the external air. The necessity for extreme precaution in the operation of annealing will be manifest if we reflect on one of the accidents which happened. On a certain occasion, after the cooling of a great casting had been completed, it was found, on withdrawing the speculum, that it was cracked into two pieces.

Lord Rosse's Telescope.

This mishap was eventually traced to the fact that one of the walls of the oven had only a single brick in its thickness, and that therefore the heat had escaped more easily through that side than through the other sides which were built of double thickness. The speculum had, consequently, not cooled uniformly, and hence the fracture had resulted. Undeterred, however, by this failure, as well as by not a few other difficulties, into a description of which we cannot now enter, Lord Rosse steadily adhered to his self-imposed task, and at last succeeded in casting two perfect discs on which to commence the tedious processes of grinding and polishing. The magnitude of the operations involved may perhaps be appreciated if I mention that the value of the mere copper and tin entering into the composition of each of the mirrors was about 500 pounds.

In no part of his undertaking was Lord Rosse's mechanical ingenuity more taxed than in the devising of the mechanism for carrying out the delicate operations of grinding and polishing the mirrors, whose casting we have just mentioned. In the ordinary operations of the telescope-maker, such processes had hitherto been generally effected by hand, but, of course, such methods became impossible when dealing with mirrors which were as large as a good-sized dinner table, and whose weight was measured by tons. The rough grinding was effected by means of a tool of cast iron about the same size as the mirror, which was moved by suitable machinery both backwards and forwards, and round and round, plenty of sand and water being supplied between the mirror and the tool to produce the necessary attrition. As the process proceeded and as the surface became smooth, emery was used instead of sand; and when this stage was complete, the grinding tool was removed and the polishing tool was substituted. The essential part of this was a surface of pitch, which, having been temporarily softened by heat, was then placed on the mirror, and accepted from the mirror the proper form. Rouge was then introduced as the polishing powder, and the operation was continued about nine hours, by which time the great mirror had acquired the appearance of highly polished silver. When completed, the disc of speculum metal was about six feet across and four inches thick. The depression in the centre was about half an inch. Mounted on a little truck, the great speculum was then conveyed to the instrument, to be placed in its receptacle at the bottom of the tube, the length of which was sixty feet, this being the focal distance of the mirror. Another small reflector was inserted in the great tube sideways, so as to direct the gaze of the observer down upon the great reflector. Thus was completed the most colossal instrument for the exploration of the heavens which the art of man has ever constructed.

It was once my privilege to be one of those to whom the illustrious builder of the great telescope entrusted its use. For two seasons in 1865 and 1866 I had the honour of being Lord Rosse's astronomer. During that time I passed many a fine night in the observer's gallery, examining different objects in the heavens with the aid of this remarkable instrument. At the time I was there, the objects principally studied were the nebulae, those faint stains of light which lie on the background of the sky. Lord Rosse's telescope was specially suited for the scrutiny of these objects, inasmuch as their delicacy required all the light-grasping power which could be provided.

One of the greatest discoveries made by Lord Rosse, when his huge instrument was first turned towards the heavens, consisted in the detection of the spiral character of some of the nebulous forms. When the extraordinary structure of these objects was first announced, the discovery was received with some degree of incredulity. Other astronomers looked at the same objects, and when they failed to discern—and they frequently did fail to discern—the spiral structure which Lord Rosse had indicated, they drew the conclusion that this spiral structure did not exist. They thought it must be due possibly to some instrumental defect or to the imagination of the observer. It was, however, hardly possible for any one who was both willing and competent to examine into the evidence, to doubt the reality of Lord Rosse's discoveries. It happens, however, that they have been recently placed beyond all doubt by testimony which it is impossible to gainsay. A witness never influenced by imagination has now come forward, and the infallible photographic plate has justified Lord Rosse. Among the remarkable discoveries which Dr. Isaac Roberts has recently made in the application of his photographic apparatus to the heavens, there is none more striking than that which declares, not only that the nebulae which Lord Rosse described as spirals, actually do possess the character so indicated, but that there are many others of the same description. He has even brought to light the astonishingly interesting fact that there are invisible objects of this class which have never been seen by human eye, but whose spiral character is visible to the peculiar delicacy of the photographic telescope.

In his earlier years, Lord Rosse himself used to be a diligent observer of the heavenly bodies with the great telescope which was completed in the year 1845. But I think that those who knew Lord Rosse well, will agree that it was more the mechanical processes incidental to the making of the telescope which engaged his interest than the actual observations with the telescope when it was completed. Indeed one who was well acquainted with him believed Lord Rosse's special interest in the great telescope ceased when the last nail had been driven into it. But the telescope was never allowed to lie idle, for Lord Rosse always had associated with him some ardent young astronomer, whose delight it was to employ to the uttermost the advantages of his position in exploring the wonders of the sky. Among those who were in this capacity in the early days of the great telescope, I may mention my esteemed friend Dr. Johnston Stoney.

Such was the renown of Lord Rosse himself, brought about by his consummate mechanical genius and his astronomical discoveries, and such the interest which gathered around the marvellous workshops at Birr castle, wherein his monumental exhibitions of optical skill were constructed, that visitors thronged to see him from all parts of the world. His home at Parsonstown became one of the most remarkable scientific centres in Great Britain; thither assembled from time to time all the leading men of science in the country, as well as many illustrious foreigners. For many years Lord Rosse filled with marked distinction the exalted position of President of the Royal Society, and his advice and experience in practical mechanical matters were always at the disposal of those who sought his assistance. Personally and socially Lord Rosse endeared himself to all with whom he came in contact. I remember one of the attendants telling me that on one occasion he had the misfortune to let fall and break one of the small mirrors on which Lord Rosse had himself expended many hours of hard personal labour. The only remark of his lordship was that "accidents will happen."

The latter years of his life Lord Rosse passed in comparative seclusion; he occasionally went to London for a brief sojourn during the season, and he occasionally went for a cruise in his yacht; but the

ROMAN CATHOLIC CHURCH AT PARSONSTOWN.

greater part of the year he spent at Birr Castle, devoting himself largely to the study of political and social questions, and rarely going outside the walls of his demesne, except to church on Sunday mornings. He died on October 31, 1867.

He was succeeded by his eldest son, the present Earl of Rosse, who has inherited his father's scientific abilities, and done much notable work with the great telescope.

AIRY.

In our sketch of the life of Flamsteed, we have referred to the circumstances under which the famous Observatory that crowns Greenwich Hill was founded. We have also had occasion to mention that among the illustrious successors of Flamsteed both Halley and Bradley are to be included. But a remarkable development of Greenwich Observatory from the modest establishment of early days took place under the direction of the distinguished astronomer whose name is at the head of this chapter. By his labours this temple of science was organised to such a degree of perfection that it has served in many respects as a model for other astronomical establishments in various parts of the world. An excellent account of Airy's career has been given by Professor H. H. Turner, in the obituary notice published by the Royal Astronomical Society. To this I am indebted for many of the particulars here to be set down concerning the life of the illustrious Astronomer Royal.

The family from which Airy took his origin came from Kentmere, in Westmoreland. His father, William Airy, belonged to a Lincolnshire branch of the same stock. His mother's maiden name was Ann Biddell, and her family resided at Playford, near Ipswich. William Airy held some small government post which necessitated an occasional change of residence to different parts of the country, and thus it was that his son, George Biddell, came to be born at Alnwick, on 27th July, 1801. The boy's education, so far as his school life was concerned was partly conducted at Hereford and partly at Colchester. He does not, however, seem to have derived much benefit from the hours which he passed in the schoolroom. But it was delightful to him to spend his holidays on the farm at Playford, where his uncle, Arthur Biddell, showed him much kindness. The scenes of his early youth remained dear to Airy throughout his life, and in subsequent years he himself owned a house at Playford, to which it was his special delight to resort for relaxation during the course of his arduous career. In spite of the defects of his school training he seems to have manifested such remarkable abilities that his uncle decided to enter him in Cambridge University. He accordingly joined Trinity College as a sizar in 1819, and after a brilliant career in mathematical and physical science he graduated as Senior Wrangler in 1823. It may be noted as an exceptional circumstance that, notwithstanding the demands on his time in studying for his tripos, he was able, after his second term of residence, to support himself entirely by taking private pupils. In the year after he had taken his degree he was elected to a Fellowship at Trinity College.

Having thus gained an independent position, Airy immediately entered upon that career of scientific work which he prosecuted without intermission almost to the very close of his life. One of his most interesting researches in these early days is on the subject of Astigmatism, which defect he had discovered in his own eyes. His investigations led him to suggest a means of correcting this defect by using a pair of spectacles with lenses so shaped as to counteract the derangement which the astigmatic eye impressed upon the rays of light. His researches on this subject were of a very complete character, and the principles he laid down are to the present day practically employed by oculists in the treatment of this malformation.

On the 7th of December, 1826, Airy was elected to the Lucasian Professorship of Mathematics in the University of Cambridge, the chair which Newton's occupancy had rendered so illustrious. His tenure of this office only lasted for two years, when he exchanged it for the Plumian Professorship. The attraction which led him to desire this change is doubtless to be found in the circumstance that the Plumian Professorship of Astronomy carried with it at that time the appointment of director of the new astronomical observatory, the origin of which must now be described.

Those most interested in the scientific side of University life decided in 1820 that it would be proper to found an astronomical observatory at Cambridge. Donations were accordingly sought for this purpose, and upwards of 6,000 pounds were contributed by members of the University and the public. To this sum 5,000 pounds were added by a grant from the University chest, and in 1824 further sums amounting altogether to 7,115 pounds were given by the University for the same object. The regulations as to the administration of the new observatory placed it under the management of the Plumian Professor, who was to be provided with two assistants. Their duties were to consist in making meridian observations of the sun, moon, and the stars, and the observations made each year were to be printed and published. The observatory was also to be used in the educational work of the University, for it was arranged that smaller instruments were to be provided by which students could be instructed in the practical art of making astronomical observations.

The building of the Cambridge Astronomical Observatory was completed in 1824, but in 1828, when Airy entered on the discharge of his duties as Director, the establishment was still far from completion, in so far as its organisation was concerned. Airy commenced his work so energetically that in the next year after his appointment he was able to publish the first volume of "Cambridge Astronomical Observations," notwithstanding that every part of the work, from the making of observations to the revising of the proof-sheets, had to be done by himself.

It may here be remarked that these early volumes of the publications of the Cambridge Observatory contained the first exposition of those systematic methods of astronomical work which Airy afterwards developed to such a great extent at Greenwich, and which have been subsequently adopted in many other places. No more profitable instruction for the astronomical beginner can be found than that which can be had by the study of these volumes, in which the Plumian Professor has laid down with admirable clearness the true principles on which meridian work should be conducted.

Airy gradually added to the instruments with which the observatory was originally equipped. A mural circle was mounted in 1832, and in the same year a small equatorial was erected by Jones. This was made use of by Airy in a well-known series of observations of Jupiter's fourth satellite for the determination of the mass of the great planet. His memoir on this subject fully ex pounds the method of finding the weight of a planet from observations of the movements of a satellite by which the planet is attended. This is, indeed, a valuable investigation

SIR GEORGE AIRY.

which no student of astronomy can afford to neglect. The ardour with which Airy devoted himself to astronomical studies may be gathered from a remarkable report on the progress of astronomy during the present century, which he communicated to the British Association at its second meeting in 1832. In the early years of his life at Cambridge his most famous achievement was connected with a research in theoretical astronomy for which consummate mathematical power was required. We can only give a brief account of the Subject, for to enter into any full detail with regard to it would be quite out of the question.

Venus is a planet of about the same size and the same weight as the earth, revolving in an orbit which lies within that described by our globe. Venus, consequently, takes less time than the earth to accomplish one revolution round the sun, and it happens that the relative movements of Venus and the earth are so proportioned that in the time in which our earth accomplishes eight of her revolutions the other planet will have accomplished almost exactly thirteen. It, therefore, follows that if the earth and Venus are in line with the sun at one date, then in eight years later both planets will again be found at the same points in their orbits. In those eight years the earth has gone round eight times, and has, therefore, regained its original position, while in the same period Venus has accomplished thirteen complete revolutions, and, therefore, this planet also has reached the same spot where it was at first. Venus and the earth, of course, attract each other, and in consequence of these mutual attractions the earth is swayed from the elliptic track which it would otherwise pursue. In like manner Venus is also forced by the attraction of the earth to revolve in a track which deviates from that which it would otherwise follow. Owing to the fact that the sun is of such preponderating magnitude (being, in fact, upwards of 300,000 times as heavy as either Venus or the earth), the disturbances induced in the motion of either planet, in consequence of the attraction of the other, are relatively insignificant to the main controlling agency by which each of the movements is governed. It is, however, possible under certain circumstances that the disturbing effects produced upon one planet by the other can become so multiplied as to produce peculiar effects which attain measurable dimensions. Suppose that the periodic times in which the earth and Venus revolved had no simple relation to each other, then the points of their tracks in which the two planets came into line with the sun would be found at different parts of the orbits, and consequently the disturbances would to a great extent neutralise each other, and produce but little appreciable effect. As, however, Venus and the earth come back every eight years to nearly the same positions at the same points of their track, an accumulative effect is produced. For the disturbance of one planet upon the other will, of course, be greatest when those two planets are nearest, that is, when they lie in line with the sun and on the same side of it. Every eight years a certain part of the orbit of the earth is, therefore, disturbed by the attraction of Venus with peculiar vigour.

The consequence is that, owing to the numerical relation between the movements of the planets to which I have referred, disturbing effects become appreciable which would otherwise be too small to permit of recognition. Airy proposed to himself to compute the effects which Venus would have on the movement of the earth in consequence of the circumstance that eight revolutions of the one planet required almost the same time as thirteen revolutions of the other. This is a mathematical inquiry of the most arduous description, but the Plumian Professor succeeded in working it out, and he had, accordingly, the gratification of announcing to the Royal Society that he had detected the influence which Venus was thus able to assert on the movement of our earth around the sun. This remarkable investigation gained for its author the gold medal of the Royal Astronomical Society in the year 1832.

In consequence of his numerous discoveries, Airy's scientific fame had become so well recognised that the Government awarded him a special pension, and in 1835, when Pond, who was then Astronomer Royal, resigned, Airy was offered the post at Greenwich. There was in truth, no scientific inducement to the Plumian Professor to leave the comparatively easy post he held at Cambridge, in which he had ample leisure to devote himself to those researches which specially interested him, and accept that of the much more arduous observatory at Greenwich. There were not even pecuniary inducements to make the change; however, he felt it to be his duty to accede to the request which the Government had made that he would take up the position which Pond had vacated, and accordingly Airy went to Greenwich as Astronomer Royal on October 1st, 1835.

He immediately began with his usual energy to organise the systematic conduct of the business of the National Observatory. To realise one of the main characteristics of Airy's great work at Greenwich, it is necessary to explain a point that might not perhaps be understood without a little explanation by those who have no practical experience in an observatory. In the work of an establishment such as Greenwich, an observation almost always consists of a measurement of some kind. The observer may, for instance, be making a measurement of the time at which a star passes across a spider line stretched through the field of view; on another occasion his object may be the measurement of an angle which is read off by examining through a microscope the lines of division on a graduated circle when the telescope is so pointed that the star is placed on a certain mark in the field of view. In either case the immediate result of the astronomical observation is a purely numerical one, but it rarely happens, indeed we may say it never happens, that the immediate numerical result which the observation gives expresses directly the quantity which we are really seeking for. No doubt the observation has been so designed that the quantity we want to find can be obtained from the figures which the measurement gives, but the object sought is not those figures, for there are always a multitude of other influences by which those figures are affected. For example, if an observation were to be perfect, then the telescope with which the observation is made should be perfectly placed in the exact position which it ought to occupy; this is, however, never the case, for no mechanic can ever construct or adjust a telescope so perfectly as the wants of the astronomer demand. The clock also by which we determine the time of the observation should be correct, but this is rarely if ever the case. We have to correct our observations for such errors, that is to say, we have to determine the errors in the positions of our telescopes and the errors in the going of our clocks, and then we have to determine what the observations would have been had our telescopes been absolutely perfect, and had our clocks been absolutely correct. There are also many other matters which have to be attended to in order to reduce our observations so as to obtain from the figures as yielded to the observer at the telescope the actual quantities which it is his object to determine.

The work of effecting these reductions is generally a very intricate and laborious matter, so that it has not unfrequently happened that while observations have accumulated in an observatory, yet the tedious duty of reducing these observations has been allowed to fall into arrear. When Airy entered on his duties at Greenwich he found there an enormous mass of observations which, though implicitly containing materials of the greatest value to astronomers, were, in their unreduced form, entirely unavailable for any useful purpose. He, therefore, devoted himself to coping with the reduction of the observations of his predecessors. He framed systematic methods by which the reductions were to be effected, and he so arranged the work that little more than careful attention to numerical accuracy would be required for the conduct of the operations. Encouraged by the Admiralty, for it is under this department that Greenwich Observatory is placed, the Astronomer Royal employed a large force of computers to deal with the work. BY his energy and admirable organisation he managed to reduce an extremely valuable series of planetary observations, and to publish the results, which have been of the greatest importance to astronomical investigation.

The Astronomer Royal was a capable, practical engineer as well as an optician, and he presently occupied himself by designing astronomical instruments of improved pattern, which should replace the antiquated instruments he found in the observatory. In the course of years the entire equipment underwent a total transformation. He ordered a great meridian circle, every part of which may be said to have been formed from his own designs. He also designed the mounting for a fine equatorial telescope worked by a driving clock, which he had himself invented. Gradually the establishment at Greenwich waxed great under his incessant care. It was the custom for the observatory to be inspected every year by a board of visitors, whose chairman was the President of the Royal Society. At each annual visitation, held on the first Saturday in June, the visitors received a report from the Astronomer Royal, in which he set forth the business which had been accomplished during the past year. It was on these occasions that applications were made to the Admiralty, either for new instruments or for developing the work of the observatory in some other way. After the more official business of the inspection was over, the observatory was thrown open to visitors, and hundreds of people enjoyed on that day the privilege of seeing the national observatory. These annual gatherings are happily still continued, and the first Saturday in June is known to be the occasion of one of the most interesting reunions of scientific men which takes place in the course of the year.

Airy's scientific work was, however, by no means confined to the observatory. He interested himself largely in expeditions for the observation of eclipses and in projects for the measurement of arcs on the earth. He devoted much attention to the collection of magnetic observations from various parts of the world. Especially will it be remembered that the circumstances of the transits of Venus, which occurred in 1874 and in 1882, were investigated by him, and under his guidance expeditions were sent forth to observe the transits from those localities in remote parts of the earth where observations most suitable for the determination of the sun's distance from the earth could be obtained. The Astronomer Royal also studied tidal phenomena, and he rendered great service to the country in the restoration of the standards of length and weight which had been destroyed in the great fire at the House of Parliament in October, 1834. In the most practical scientific matters his advice was often sought, and was as cheerfully rendered. Now we find him engaged in an investigation of the irregularities of the compass in iron ships, with a view to remedying its defects; now we find him reporting on the best gauge for railways. Among the most generally useful developments of the observatory must be mentioned the telegraphic method for the distribution of exact time. By arrangement with the Post Office, the astronomers at Greenwich despatch each morning a signal from the observatory to London at ten o'clock precisely. By special apparatus, this signal is thence distributed automatically over the country, so as to enable the time to be known everywhere accurately to a single second. It was part of the same system that a time ball should be dropped daily at one o'clock at Deal, as well as at other places, for the purpose of enabling ship's chronometers to be regulated.

Airy's writings were most voluminous, and no fewer than forty-eight memoirs by him are mentioned in the "Catalogue of Scientific Memoirs," published by the Royal Society up to the year 1873, and this only included ten years out of an entire life of most extraordinary activity. Many other subjects besides those of a purely scientific character from time to time engaged his attention. He wrote, for instance, a very interesting treatise on the Roman invasion of Britain, especially with a view of determining the port from which Caesar set forth from Gaul, and the point at which he landed on the British coast. Airy was doubtless led to this investigation by his study of the tidal phenomena in the Straits of Dover. Perhaps the Astronomer Royal is best known to the general reading public by his excellent lectures on astronomy, delivered at the Ipswich Museum in 1848. This book has passed through many editions, and it gives a most admirable account of the manner in which the fundamental problems in astronomy have to be attacked.

As years rolled by almost every honour and distinction that could be conferred upon a scientific man was awarded to Sir George Airy. He was, indeed, the recipient of other honours not often awarded for scientific distinction. Among these we may mention that in 1875 he received the freedom of the City of London, "as a recognition of his indefatigable labours in astronomy, and of his eminent services in the advancement of practical science, whereby he has so materially benefited the cause of commerce and civilisation."

Until his eightieth year Airy continued to discharge his labours at Greenwich with unflagging energy. At last, on August 15th, 1881, he resigned the office which he had held so long with such distinction to himself and such benefit to his country. He had married in 1830 the daughter of the Rev. Richard Smith, of Edensor. Lady Airy died in 1875, and three sons and three daughters survived him. One daughter is the wife of Dr. Routh, of Cambridge, and his other daughters were the constant companions of their father during the declining years of his life. Up to the age of ninety he enjoyed perfect physical health, but an accidental fall which then occurred was attended with serious results. He died on Saturday, January 2nd, 1892, and was buried in the churchyard at Playford.

HAMILTON.

William Rowan Hamilton was born at midnight between the 3rd and 4th of August, 1805, at Dublin, in the house which was then 29, but subsequently 36, Dominick Street. His father, Archibald Hamilton, was a solicitor, and William was the fourth of a family of nine. With reference to his descent, it may be sufficient to notice that his ancestors appear to have been chiefly of gentle Irish families, but that his maternal grandmother was of Scottish birth. When he was about a year old, his father and mother decided to hand over the education of the child to his uncle, James Hamilton, a clergyman of Trim, in County Meath. James Hamilton's sister, Sydney, resided with him, and it was in their home that the days of William's childhood were passed.

In Mr. Graves' "Life of Sir William Rowan Hamilton" a series of letters will be found, in which Aunt Sydney details the progress of the boy to his mother in Dublin. Probably there is no record of an infant prodigy more extraordinary than that which these letters contain. At three years old his aunt assured the mother that William is "a hopeful blade," but at that time it was his physical vigour to which she apparently referred; for the proofs of his capacity, which she adduces, related to his prowess in making boys older than himself fly before him. In the second letter, a month later, we hear that William is brought in to read the Bible for the purpose of putting to shame other boys double his age who could not read nearly so well. Uncle James appears to have taken much pains with William's schooling, but his aunt said that "how he picks up everything is astonishing, for he never stops playing and jumping about." When he was four years and three months old, we hear that he went out to dine at the vicar's, and amused the company by reading for them equally well whether the book was turned upside down or held in any other fashion. His aunt assures the mother that "Willie is a most sensible little creature, but at the same time has a great deal of roguery." At four years and five months old he came up to pay his mother a visit in town, and she writes to her sister a description of the boy;—

"His reciting is astonishing, and his clear and accurate knowledge of geography is beyond belief; he even draws the countries with a pencil on paper, and will cut them out, though not perfectly accurate, yet so well that a anybody knowing the countries could not mistake them; but, you will think this nothing when I tell you that he reads Latin, Greek, and Hebrew."

Aunt Sydney recorded that the moment Willie got back to Trim he was desirous of at once resuming his former pursuits. He would not eat his breakfast till his uncle had heard him his Hebrew, and he comments on the importance of proper pronunciation. At five he was taken to see a friend, to whom he repeated long passages from Dryden. A gentleman present, who was not unnaturally sceptical about Willie's attainments, desired to test him in Greek, and took down a copy of Homer which happened to have the contracted type, and to his amazement Willie went on with the greatest ease. At six years and nine months he was translating Homer and Virgil; a year later his uncle tells us that William finds so little difficulty in learning French and Italian, that he wishes to read Homer in French. He is enraptured with the Iliad, and carries it about with him, repeating from it whatever particularly pleases him. At eight years and one month the boy was one of a party who visited the Scalp in the Dublin mountains, and he was so delighted with the scenery that he forthwith delivered an oration in Latin. At nine years and six months he is not satisfied until he learns Sanscrit; three months later his thirst for the Oriental languages is unabated, and at ten years and four months he is studying Arabic and Persian. When nearly twelve he prepared a manuscript ready for publication. It was a "Syriac Grammar," in Syriac letters and characters compiled from that of Buxtorf, by William Hamilton, Esq., of Dublin and Trim. When he was fourteen, the Persian ambassador, Mirza Abul Hassan Khan, paid a visit to Dublin, and, as a practical exercise in his Oriental languages, the young scholar addressed to his Excellency a letter in Persian; a translation of which production is given by Mr. Graves. When William was fourteen he had the misfortune to lose his father; and he had lost his mother two years previously. The boy and his three sisters were kindly provided for by different members of the family on both sides.

It was when William was about fifteen that his attention began to be turned towards scientific subjects. These were at first regarded rather as a relaxation from the linguistic studies with which he had been so largely occupied. On November 22nd, 1820, he notes in his journal that he had begun Newton's "Principia": he commenced also the study of astronomy by observing eclipses, occultations, and similar phenomena. When he was sixteen we learn that he had read conic sections, and that he was engaged in the study of pendulums. After an attack of illness, he was moved for change to Dublin, and in May, 1822, we find him reading the differential calculus and Laplace's "Mecanique Celeste." He criticises an important part of Laplace's work relative to the demonstration of the parallelogram of forces. In this same year appeared the first gushes of those poems which afterwards flowed in torrents.

His somewhat discursive studies had, however, now to give place to a more definite course of reading in preparation for entrance to the University of Dublin. The tutor under whom he entered, Charles Boyton, was himself a distinguished man, but he frankly told the young William that he could be of little use to him as a tutor, for his pupil was quite as fit to be his tutor. Eliza Hamilton, by whom this is recorded, adds, "But there is one thing which Boyton would promise to be to him, and that was a *friend*; and that one proof he would give of this should be that, if ever he saw William beginning to be *upset* by the sensation he would excite, and the notice he would attract, he would tell him of it." At the beginning of his college career he distanced all his competitors in every intellectual pursuit. At his first term examination in the University he was first in Classics and first in Mathematics, while he received the Chancellor's prize for a poem on the Ionian Islands, and another for his poem on Eustace de St. Pierre.

There is abundant testimony that Hamilton had "a heart for friendship formed." Among the warmest of the friends whom he made in these early days was the gifted Maria Edgeworth, who writes to her sister about "young Mr. Hamilton, an admirable Crichton of eighteen, a real prodigy of talents, who Dr. Brinkley says may be a second Newton, quiet, gentle, and simple." His sister Eliza, to whom he was affectionately attached, writes to him in 1824:—

"I had been drawing pictures of you in my mind in your study at Cumberland Street with 'Xenophon,' &c., on the table, and you, with your most awfully sublime face of thought, now sitting down, and now walking about, at times rubbing your hands with an air of satisfaction, and at times bursting forth into some very heroical strain of poetry in an unknown language, and in your own internal solemn ventriloquist-like voice, when you address yourself to the silence and solitude of your own room, and indeed, at times, even when your mysterious poetical addresses are not quite unheard."

This letter is quoted because it refers to a circumstance which all who ever met with Hamilton, even in his latest years, will remember. He was endowed with two distinct voices, one a high treble, the other a deep bass, and he alternately employed these voices not only in ordinary conversation, but when he was delivering an address on the profundities of Quaternions to the Royal Irish Academy, or on similar occasions. His friends had long grown so familiar with this peculiarity that they were sometimes rather surprised to find how ludicrous it appeared to strangers.

Hamilton was fortunate in finding, while still at a very early age, a career open before him which was worthy of his talents. He had not ceased to be an undergraduate before he was called to fill an illustrious chair in his university. The circumstances are briefly as follows.

We have already mentioned that, in 1826, Brinkley was appointed Bishop of Cloyne, and the professorship of astronomy thereupon became vacant. Such was Hamilton's conspicuous eminence that, notwithstanding he was still an undergraduate, and had only just completed his twenty-first year, he was immediately thought of as a suitable successor to the chair. Indeed, so remarkable were his talents in almost every direction that had the vacancy been in the professorship of classics or of mathematics, of English literature or of metaphysics, of modern or of Oriental languages, it seems difficult to suppose that he would not have occurred to every one as a possible successor. The chief ground, however, on which the friends of Hamilton urged his appointment was the earnest of original power which he had already shown in a research on the theory of Systems of Rays. This profound work created a new branch of optics, and led a few years later to a superb discovery, by which the fame of its author became world-wide.

At first Hamilton thought it would be presumption for him to apply for so exalted a position; he accordingly retired to the country, and resumed his studies for his degree. Other eminent candidates came forward, among them some from Cambridge, and a few of the Fellows from Trinity College, Dublin, also sent in their claims. It was not until Hamilton received an urgent letter from his tutor Boyton, in which he was assured of the favourable disposition of the Board towards his candidature, that he consented to come forward, and on June 16th, 1827, he was unanimously chosen to succeed the Bishop of Cloyne as Professor of Astronomy in the University. The appointment met with almost universal approval. It should, however, be noted that Brinkley, whom Hamilton succeeded, did not concur in the general sentiment. No one could have formed a higher opinion than he had done of Hamilton's transcendent powers; indeed, it was on that very ground that he seemed to view the appointment with disapprobation. He considered that it would have been wiser for Hamilton to have obtained a Fellowship, in which capacity he would have been able to exercise a greater freedom in his choice of intellectual pursuits. The bishop seems to have thought, and not without reason, that Hamilton's genius would rather recoil from much of the routine work of an astronomical establishment. Now that Hamilton's whole life is before us, it is easy to see that the bishop was entirely wrong. It is quite true that Hamilton never became a skilled astronomical observer; but the seclusion of the observatory was eminently favourable to those gigantic labours to which his life was devoted, and which have shed so much lustre, not only on Hamilton himself, but also on his University and his country.

In his early years at Dunsink, Hamilton did make some attempts at a practical use of the telescopes, but he possessed no natural aptitude for such work, while exposure which it involved seems to have acted injuriously on his health. He, therefore, gradually allowed his attention to be devoted to those mathematical researches in which he had already given such promise of distinction. Although it was in pure mathematics that he ultimately won his greatest fame, yet he always maintained and maintained with justice, that he had ample claims to the title of an astronomer. In his later years he set forth this position himself in a rather striking manner. De Morgan had written commending to Hamilton's notice Grant's "History of Physical Astronomy." After becoming acquainted with the book, Hamilton writes to his friend as follows:—

"The book is very valuable, and very creditable to its composer. But your humble servant may be pardoned if he finds himself somewhat amused at the title, 'History of Physical Astronomy from the Earliest Ages to the Middle of the Nineteenth Century,' when he fails to observe any notice of the discoveries of Sir W. R. Hamilton in the theory of the 'Dynamics of the Heavens.'"

The intimacy between the two correspondents will account for the tone of this letter; and, indeed, Hamilton supplies in the lines which follow ample grounds for his complaint. He tells how Jacobi spoke of him in Manchester in 1842 as "le Lagrange de votre pays," and how Donkin had said that, "The Analytical Theory of Dynamics as it exists at present is due mainly to the labours of La Grange Poisson, Sir W. R. Hamilton, and Jacobi, whose researches on this subject present a series of discoveries hardly paralleled for their elegance and importance in any other branch of mathematics." In the same letter Hamilton also alludes to the success which had attended the applications of his methods in other hands than his own to the elucidation of the difficult subject of Planetary Perturbations. Even had his contributions to science amounted to no more than these discoveries, his tenure of the chair would have been an illustrious one. It happens, however, that in the gigantic mass of his intellectual work these researches, though intrinsically of such importance, assume what might almost be described as a relative insignificance.

The most famous achievement of Hamilton's earlier years at the observatory was the discovery of conical refraction. This was one of those rare events in the history of science, in which a sagacious calculation has predicted a result of an almost startling character, subsequently confirmed by observation. At once this conferred on the young professor a world-wide renown. Indeed, though he was still only twenty-seven, he had already lived through an amount of intellectual activity which would have been remarkable for a man of threescore and ten.

Simultaneously with his growth in fame came the growth of his several friendships. There were, in the first place, his scientific friendships with Herschel, Robinson, and many others with whom he had copious correspondence. In the excellent biography to which I have referred, Hamilton's correspondence with Coleridge may be read, as can also the letters to his lady correspondents, among them being Maria Edgeworth, Lady Dunraven, and Lady Campbell. Many of these sheets relate to literary matters, but they are largely intermingled With genial pleasantry, and serve at all events to show the affection and esteem with which he was regarded by all who had the privilege of knowing him. There are also the letters to the sisters whom he adored, letters brimming over with such exalted sentiment, that most ordinary sisters would be tempted to receive them with a smile in the excessively improbable event of their still more ordinary brothers attempting to pen such effusions. There are also indications of letters to and from other young ladies who from time to time were the objects of Hamilton's tender admiration. We use the plural advisedly, for, as Mr. Graves has set forth, Hamilton's love affairs pursued a rather troubled course. The attention which he lavished on one or two fair ones was not reciprocated, and even the intense charms of mathematical discovery could not assuage the pangs which the disappointed lover experienced. At last he reached the haven of matrimony in 1833, when he was married to Miss Bayly. Of his married life Hamilton said, many years later to De Morgan, that it was as happy as he expected, and happier than he deserved. He had two sons, William and Archibald, and one daughter, Helen, who became the wife of Archdeacon O'Regan.

The most remarkable of Hamilton's friendships in his early years was unquestionably that with Wordsworth. It commenced with Hamilton's visit to Keswick; and on the first evening, when the poet met the young mathematician, an incident occurred which showed the mutual interest that was aroused. Hamilton thus describes it in a letter to his sister Eliza:

"He (Wordsworth) walked back with our party as far as their lodge, and then, on our bidding Mrs. Harrison good-night, I offered to walk back with him while my party proceeded to the hotel. This offer he ac-

SIR W. ROWAN HAMILTON.

cepted, and our conversation had become so interesting that when we had arrived at his home, a distance of about a mile, he proposed to walk back with me on my way to Ambleside, a proposal which you may be sure I did not reject; so far from it that when he came to turn once more towards his home I also turned once more along with him. It was very late when I reached the hotel after all this walking."

Hamilton also submitted to Wordsworth an original poem, entitled "It Haunts me Yet." The reply of Wordsworth is worth repeating:—

"With a safe conscience I can assure you that, in my judgment, your verses are animated with the poetic spirit, as they are evidently the product of strong feeling. The sixth and seventh stanzas affected me much, even to the dimming of my eyes and faltering of my voice while I was reading them aloud. Having said this, I have said enough. Now for the per contra. You will not, I am sure, be hurt when I tell you that the workmanship (what else could be expected from so young a writer?) is not what it ought to be. . .

"My household desire to be remembered to you in no formal way. Seldom have I parted—never, I was going to say—with one whom after so short an acquaintance I lost sight of with more regret. I trust we shall meet again."

The further affectionate intercourse between Hamilton and Wordsworth is fully set forth, and to Hamilton's latest years a recollection of his "Rydal hours" was carefully treasured and frequently referred to. Wordsworth visited Hamilton at the observatory, where a beautiful shady path in the garden is to the present day spoken of as "Words-worth's Walk."

It was the practice of Hamilton to produce a sonnet on almost every occasion which admitted of poetical treatment, and it was his delight to communicate his verses to his friends all round. When Whewell was producing his "Bridgewater Treatises," he writes to Hamilton in 1833:—

"Your sonnet which you showed me expressed much better than I could express it the feeling with which I tried to write this book, and I once intended to ask your permission to prefix the sonnet to my book, but my friends persuaded me that I ought to tell my story in my own prose, however much better your verse might be."

The first epoch-marking contribution to Theoretical Dynamics after the time of Newton was undoubtedly made by Lagrange, in his discovery of the general equations of Motion. The next great step in the same direction was that taken by Hamilton in his discovery of a still more comprehensive method. Of this contribution Hamilton writes to Whewell, March 31st, 1834:—

"As to my late paper, a day or two ago sent off to London, it is merely mathematical and deductive. I ventured, indeed, to call it the 'Mecanique Analytique' of Lagrange, 'a scientific poem'; and spoke of Dynamics, or the Science of Force, as treating of 'Power acting by Law in Space and Time.' In other respects it is as unpoetical and unmeta-physical as my gravest friends could desire."

It may well be doubted whether there is a more beautiful chapter in the whole of mathematical philosophy than that which contains Hamilton's dynamical theory. It is disfigured by no tedious complexity of symbols; it condescends not to any particular problems; it is an all embracing theory, which gives an intellectual grasp of the most appro-priate method for discovering the result of the application of force to matter. It is the very generality of this doctrine which has somewhat impeded the applications of which it is susceptible. The exigencies of examinations are partly responsible for the fact that the method has not become more familiar to students of the higher mathematics. An eminent professor has complained that Hamilton's essay on dynamics was of such an extremely abstract character, that he found himself un-able to extract from it problems suitable for his examination papers.

The following extract is from a letter of Professor Sylvester to Hamilton, dated 20th of September, 1841. It will show how his works were appreciated by so consummate a mathematician as the writer:—

"Believe me, sir, it is not the least of my regrets in quitting this em-pire to feel that I forego the casual occasion of meeting those masters of my art, yourself chief amongst the number, whose acquaintance, whose conversation, or even notice, have in themselves the power to inspire, and almost to impart fresh vigour to the understanding, and the courage and faith without which the efforts of invention are in vain. The golden moments I enjoyed under your hospitable roof at Dunsink, or moments such as they were, may probably never again fall to my lot.

"At a vast distance, and in an humble eminence, I still promise my-self the calm satisfaction of observing your blazing course in the ele-vated regions of discovery. Such national honour as you are able to confer on your country is, perhaps, the only species of that luxury for the rich (I mean what is termed one's glory) which is not bought at the expense of the comforts of the million."

The study of metaphysics was always a favourite recreation when Hamilton sought for a change from the pursuit of mathematics. In the year 1834 we find him a diligent student of Kant; and, to show the views of the author of Quaternions and of Algebra as the Science of

Pure Time on the "Critique of the Pure Reason," we quote the "following letter, dated 18th of July, 1834, from Hamilton to Viscount Adare:—

"I have read a large part of the 'Critique of the Pure Reason,' and find it wonderfully clear, and generally quite convincing. Notwithstanding some previous preparation from Berkeley, and from my own thoughts, I seem to have learned much from Kant's own statement of his views of 'Space and Time.' Yet, on the whole, a large part of my pleasure consists in recognising through Kant's works, opinions, or rather views, which have been long familiar to myself, although far more clearly and systematically expressed and combined by him. . . . Kant is, I think, much more indebted than he owns, or, perhaps knows, to Berkeley, whom he calls by a sneer, '*Gutem* Berkeley'. . . as it were, 'good soul, well meaning man,' who was able for all that to shake to its centre the world of human thought, and to effect a revolution among the early consequences of which was the growth of Kant himself."

At several meetings of the British Association Hamilton was a very conspicuous figure. Especially was this the case in 1835, when the Association met in Dublin, and when Hamilton, though then but thirty years old, had attained such celebrity that even among a very brilliant gathering his name was perhaps the most renowned. A banquet was given at Trinity College in honour of the meeting. The distinguished visitors assembled in the Library of the University. The Earl of Mulgrave, then Lord Lieutenant of Ireland, made this the opportunity of conferring on Hamilton the honour of knighthood, gracefully adding, as he did so: "I but set the royal, and therefore the national mark, on a distinction already acquired by your genius and labours."

The banquet followed, writes Mr. Graves. "It was no little addition to the honour Hamilton had already received that, when Professor Whewell returned thanks for the toast of the University of Cambridge, he thought it appropriate to add the words, 'There was one point which strongly pressed upon him at that moment: it was now one hundred and thirty years since a great man in another Trinity College knelt down before his sovereign, and rose up Sir Isaac Newton.' The compliment was welcomed by immense applause."

A more substantial recognition of the labours of Hamilton took place subsequently. He thus describes it in a letter to Mr. Graves of 14th of November, 1843:—

"The Queen has been pleased—and you will not doubt that it was entirely unsolicited, and even unexpected, on my part—'to express her entire approbation of the grant of a pension of two hundred pounds per annum from the Civil List' to me for scientific services. The letters from Sir Robert Peel and from the Lord Lieutenant of Ireland in which this grant has been communicated or referred to have been really more gratifying to my feelings than the addition to my income, however useful, and almost necessary, that may have been."

The circumstances we have mentioned might lead to the supposition that Hamilton was then at the zenith of his fame but this was not so. It might more truly be said, that his achievements up to this point were rather the preliminary exercises which fitted him for the gigantic task of his life. The name of Hamilton is now chiefly associated with his memorable invention of the calculus of Quaternions. It was to the creation of this branch of mathematics that the maturer powers of his life were devoted; in fact he gives us himself an illustration of how completely habituated he became to the new modes of thought which Quaternions originated. In one of his later years he happened to take up a copy of his famous paper on Dynamics, a paper which at the time created such a sensation among mathematicians, and which is at this moment regarded as one of the classics of dynamical literature. He read, he tells us, his paper with considerable interest, and expressed his feelings of gratification that he found himself still able to follow its reasoning without undue effort. But it seemed to him all the time as a work belonging to an age of analysis now entirely superseded.

In order to realise the magnitude of the revolution which Hamilton has wrought in the application of symbols to mathematical investigation, it is necessary to think of what Hamilton did beside the mighty advance made by Descartes. To describe the character of the quaternion calculus would be unsuited to the pages of this work, but we may quote an interesting letter, written by Hamilton from his death-bed, twenty-two years later, to his son Archibald, in which he has recorded the circumstances of the discovery:—

"Indeed, I happen to be able to put the finger of memory upon the year and month—October, 1843—when having recently returned from visits to Cork and Parsonstown, connected with a meeting of the British Association, the desire to discover the laws of multiplication referred to, regained with me a certain strength and earnestness which had for years been dormant, but was then on the point of being gratified, and was occasionally talked of with you. Every morning in the early part of the above-cited month, on my coming down to breakfast, your (then) little brother William Edwin, and yourself, used to ask me, 'Well papa, can you multiply triplets?' Whereto I was always obliged to reply, with a sad shake of the head: 'No, I can only *add* and subtract them,'

"But on the 16th day of the same month—which happened to be Monday, and a Council day of the Royal Irish Academy—I was walking in to attend and preside, and your mother was walking with me along the Royal Canal, to which she had perhaps driven; and although she talked with me now and then, yet an *undercurrent* of thought was going on in my mind which gave at last a *result*, whereof it is not too much to say that I felt *at once* the importance. An *electric* circuit seemed to *close*; and a spark flashed forth the herald (as I *foresaw immediately*) of many long years to come of definitely directed thought and work by *myself*, if spared, and, at all events, on the part of *others* if I should even be allowed to live long enough distinctly to communicate the discovery. Nor could I resist the impulse—unphilosophical as it may have been—to cut with a knife on a stone of Brougham Bridge as we passed it, the fundamental formula which contains the *solution* of the *problem*, but, of course, the inscription has long since mouldered away. A more durable notice remains, however, on the Council Books of the Academy for that day (October 16, 1843), which records the fact that I then asked for and obtained leave to read a Paper on 'Quaternions,' at the First General Meeting of the Session; which reading took place accordingly, on Monday, the 13th of November following."

Writing to Professor Tait, Hamilton gives further particulars of the same event. And again in a letter to the Rev. J. W. Stubbs:—

"To-morrow will be the fifteenth birthday of the Quaternions. They started into life full-grown on the 16th October, 1843, as I was walking with Lady Hamilton to Dublin, and came up to Brougham Bridge— which my boys have since called Quaternion Bridge. I pulled out a pocketbook which still exists, and made entry, on which at the very moment I felt that it might be worth my while to expend the labour of at least ten or fifteen years to come. But then it is fair to say that this was because I felt a problem to have been at that moment solved, an intellectual want relieved which had haunted me for at least fifteen years before.

"But did the thought of establishing such a system, in which geometrically opposite facts—namely, two lines (or areas) which are opposite IN *space* give *always* a positive product—ever come into anybody's head till I was led to it in October, 1843, by trying to extend my old theory of algebraic couples, and of algebra as the science of pure time? As to my regarding geometrical addition of lines as equivalent to composition of motions (and as performed by the same rules), that is indeed essential in my theory but not peculiar to it; on the contrary, I am only one of many who have been led to this view of addition."

Pilgrims in future ages will doubtless visit the spot commemorated by the invention of Quaternions. Perhaps as they look at that by no means graceful structure Quaternion Bridge, they will regret that the hand of some Old Mortality had not been occasionally employed in cutting the memorable inscription afresh. It is now irrecoverably lost.

It was ten years after the discovery that the great volume appeared under the title of "Lectures on Quaternions," Dublin, 1853. The reception of this work by the scientific world was such as might have been expected from the extraordinary reputation of its author, and the novelty and importance of the new calculus. His valued friend, Sir John Herschel, writes to him in that style of which he was a master:—

"Now, most heartily let me congratulate you on getting out your book—on having found utterance, ore rotundo, for all that labouring and seething mass of thought which has been from time to time sending out sparks, and gleams, and smokes, and shaking the soil about you; but now breaks into a good honest eruption, with a lava stream and a shower of fertilizing ashes.

"Metaphor and simile apart, there is work for a twelve-month to any man to read such a book, and for half a lifetime to digest it, and I am glad to see it brought to a conclusion."

We may also record Hamilton's own opinion expressed to Humphrey Lloyd:—

"In general, although in one sense I hope that I am actually growing modest about the quaternions, from my seeing so many peeps and vistas into future expansions of their principles, I still must assert that this discovery appears to me to be as important for the middle of the nineteenth century as the discovery of fluxions was for the close of the seventeenth."

Bartholomew Lloyd died in 1837. He had been the Provost of Trinity College, and the President of the Royal Irish Academy. Three candidates were put forward by their respective friends for the vacant Presidency. One was Humphrey Lloyd, the son of the late Provost, and the two others were Hamilton and Archbishop Whately. Lloyd from the first urged strongly the claims of Hamilton, and deprecated the putting forward of his own name. Hamilton in like manner desired to withdraw in favour of Lloyd. The wish was strongly felt by many of the Fellows of the College that Lloyd should be elected, in consequence of his having a more intimate association with collegiate life than Hamilton; while his scientific eminence was world-wide. The election ultimately gave Hamilton a considerable majority over Lloyd, behind whom the Archbishop followed at a considerable distance. All concluded happily, for both Lloyd and the Archbishop expressed, and no doubt felt, the pre-eminent claims of Hamilton, and both of them cordially accepted the office of a Vice-President, to which, according to the constitution of the Academy, it is the privilege of the incoming President to nominate.

In another chapter I have mentioned as a memorable episode in astronomical history, that Sir J. Herschel went for a prolonged sojourn to the Cape of Good Hope, for the purpose of submitting the southern skies to the same scrutiny with the great telescope that his father had given to the northern skies. The occasion of Herschel's return after the brilliant success of his enterprise, was celebrated by a banquet. On June 15th, 1838, Hamilton was assigned the high honour of proposing the health of Herschel. This banquet is otherwise memorable in Hamilton's career as being one of the two occasions in which he was in the company of his intimate friend De Morgan.

In the year 1838 a scheme was adopted by the Royal Irish Academy for the award of medals to the authors of papers which appeared to possess exceptionally high merit. At the institution of the medal two papers were named in competition for the prize. One was Hamilton's "Memoir on Algebra, as the Science of Pure Time." The other was Macullagh's paper on the "Laws of Crystalline Reflection and Refraction." Hamilton expresses his gratification that, mainly in consequence of his own exertions, he succeeded in having the medal awarded to Macullagh rather than to himself. Indeed, it would almost appear as if Hamilton had procured a letter from Sir J. Herschel, which indicated the importance of Macullagh's memoir in such a way as to decide the issue. It then became Hamilton's duty to award the medal from the chair, and to deliver an address in which he expressed his own sense of the excellence of Macullagh's scientific work. It is the more necessary to allude to these points, because in the whole of his scientific career it would seem that Macullagh was the only man with whom Hamilton had ever even an approach to a dispute about priority. The incident referred to took place in connection with the discovery of conical refraction, the fame of which Macullagh made a preposterous attempt to wrest from Hamilton. This is evidently alluded to in Hamilton's letter to the Marquis of Northampton, dated June 28th, 1838, in which we read:—

"And though some former circumstances prevented me from applying to the person thus distinguished the sacred name of FRIEND, I had the pleasure of doing justice...to his high intellectual merits... I believe he was not only gratified but touched, and may, perhaps, regard me in future with feelings more like those which I long to entertain towards him."

Hamilton was in the habit, from time to time, of commencing the keeping of a journal, but it does not appear to have been systematically conducted. Whatever difficulties the biographer may have experienced from its imperfections and irregularities, seem to be amply compensated for by the practice which Hamilton had of preserving copies of his letters, and even of comparatively insignificant memoranda. In fact, the minuteness with which apparently trivial matters were often noted down appears almost whimsical. He frequently made a memorandum of the name of the person who carried a letter to the post, and of the hour in which it was despatched. On the other hand, the letters which he received were also carefully preserved in a mighty mass of manuscripts, with which his study was encumbered, and with which many other parts of the house were not unfrequently invaded. If a letter was laid aside for a few hours, it would become lost to view amid the seething mass of papers, though occasionally, to use his own expression, it might be seen "eddying" to the surface in some later disturbance.

The great volume of "Lectures on Quaternions" had been issued, and the author had received the honours which the completion of such a task would rightfully bring him. The publication of an immortal work does not, however, necessarily provide the means for paying the printer's bill. The printing of so robust a volume was necessarily costly; and even if all the copies could be sold, which at the time did not seem very likely, they would hardly have met the inevitable expenses. The provision of the necessary funds was, therefore, a matter for consideration. The Board of Trinity College had already contributed 200 pounds to the printing, but yet another hundred was required. Even the discoverer of Quaternions found this a source of much anxiety. However, the board, urged by the representation of Humphrey Lloyd, now one of its members, and, as we have already seen, one of Hamilton's staunchest friends, relieved him of all liability. We may here note that, notwithstanding the pension which Hamilton enjoyed in addition to the salary of his chair, he seems always to have been in some what straitened circumstances, or, to use his own words in one of his letters to De Morgan, "Though not an embarrassed man, I am anything rather than a rich one." It appears that, notwithstanding the world-wide fame of Hamilton's discoveries, the only profit in a pecuniary sense that he ever obtained from any of his works was by the sale of what he called his Icosian Game. Some enterprising publisher, on the urgent representations of one of Hamilton's friends in London, bought the copyright of the Icosian Game for 25 pounds. Even this little speculation proved unfortunate for the purchaser, as the public could not be induced to take the necessary interest in the matter.

After the completion of his great book, Hamilton appeared for awhile to permit himself a greater indulgence than usual in literary relaxations. He had copious correspondence with his intimate friend, Aubrey de Vere, and there were multitudes of letters from those troops of friends whom it was Hamilton's privilege to possess. He had been greatly affected by the death of his beloved sister Eliza, a poetess of much taste and feeling. She left to him her many papers to preserve or to destroy, but he said it was only after the expiration of four years of mourning that he took courage to open her pet box of letters.

The religious side of Hamilton's character is frequently illustrated in these letters; especially is this brought out in the correspondence with De Vere, who had seceded to the Church of Rome. Hamilton writes, August 4, 1855:—

"If, then, it be painfully evident to both, that under such circumstances there *cannot* (whatever we may both *desire*) be *now* in the nature of things, or of minds, the same degree of *intimacy* between us as of old; since we could no longer *talk* with the same degree of unreserve on every subject which happened to present itself, but *must*, from the simplest instincts of courtesy, be each on his guard not to say what might be offensive, or, at least, painful to the other; yet *we* were *once* so intimate, and retain still, and, as I trust, shall always retain, so much of regard and esteem and appreciation for each other, made tender by so many associations of my early youth and your boyhood, which can never be forgotten by either of us, that (as times go) *two or three very respectable friendships* might easily be carved out from the fragments of our former and ever-to-be-remembered *intimacy*. It would be no exaggeration to quote the words: 'Heu! quanto minus est cum reliquis versari, quam tui meminisse!'"

In 1858 a correspondence on the subject of Quaternions commenced between Professor Tait and Sir William Hamilton. It was particularly gratifying to the discoverer that so competent a mathematician as Professor Tait should have made himself acquainted with the new calculus. It is, of course, well known that Professor Tait subsequently brought out a most valuable elementary treatise on Quaternions, to which those who are anxious to become acquainted with the subject will often turn in preference to the tremendous work of Hamilton.

In the year 1861 gratifying information came to hand of the progress which the study of Quaternions was making abroad. Especially did the subject attract the attention of that accomplished mathematician, Moebius, who had already in his "Barycentrische Calculus" been led to conceptions which bore more affinity to Quaternions than could be found in the writings of any other mathematician. Such notices of his work were always pleasing to Hamilton, and they served, perhaps, as incentives to that still closer and more engrossing labour by which he became more and more absorbed. During the last few years of his life he was observed to be even more of a recluse than he had hitherto been. His powers of long and continuous study seemed to grow with advancing years, and his intervals of relaxation, such as they were, became more brief and more infrequent.

It was not unusual for him to work for twelve hours at a stretch. The dawn would frequently surprise him as he looked up to snuff his candles after a night of fascinating labour at original research. Regularity in habits was impossible to a student who had prolonged fits of what he called his mathematical trances. Hours for rest and hours for meals could only be snatched in the occasional the lucid intervals between one attack of Quaternions and the next. When hungry, he would go to see whether anything could be found on the sideboard; when thirsty, he would visit the locker, and the one blemish in the man's personal character is that these latter visits were sometimes paid too often.

As an example of one of Hamilton's rare diversions from the all-absorbing pursuit of Quaternions, we find that he was seized with curiosity to calculate back to the date of the Hegira, which he found on the 15th July, 622. He speaks of the satisfaction with which he ascertained subsequently that Herschel had assigned precisely the same date. Metaphysics remained also, as it had ever been, a favourite subject of Hamilton's readings and meditations and of correspondence with his friends. He wrote a very long letter to Dr. Ingleby on the subject of his "Introduction to Metaphysics." In it Hamilton alludes, as he has done also in other places, to a peculiarity of his own vision. It was habitual to him, by some defect in the correlation of his eyes, to see always a distinct image with each; in fact, he speaks of the remarkable effect which the use of a good stereoscope had on his sensations of vision. It was then, for the first time, that he realised how the two images which he had always seen hitherto would, under normal circumstances, be blended into one. He cites this fact as bearing on the phenomena of binocular vision, and he draws from it the inference that the necessity of binocular vision for the correct appreciation of distance is unfounded. "I am quite sure," he says, "that I *see distance* with *each eye separately.*"

The commencement of 1865, the last year of his life saw Hamilton as diligent as ever, and corresponding with Salmon and Cayley. On April 26th he writes to a friend to say, that his health has not been good for years past, and that so much work has injured his constitution; and he adds, that it is not conducive to good spirits to find that he is accumulating another heavy bill with the printer for the publication of the "Elements." This was, indeed, up to the day of his death, a cause for serious anxiety. It may, however, be mentioned that the whole cost, which amounted to nearly 500 pounds, was, like that of the previous volume, ultimately borne by the College. Contrary to anticipation, the enterprise, even in a pecuniary sense, cannot have been a very unprofitable one. The whole edition has long been out of print, and as much as 5 pounds has since been paid for a single copy.

It was on the 9th of May, 1865, that Hamilton was in Dublin for the last time. A few days later he had a violent attack of gout, and on the 4th of June he became alarmingly ill, and on the next day had an attack of epileptic convulsions. However, he slightly rallied, so that before the end of the month he was again at work at the "Elements." A gratifying incident brightened some of the last days of his life. The National Academy of Science in America had then been just formed. A list of foreign Associates had to be chosen from the whole world, and a discussion took place as to what name should be placed first on the list. Hamilton was informed by private communication that this great distinction was awarded to him by a majority of two-thirds.

In August he was still at work on the table of contents of the "Elements," and one of his very latest efforts was his letter to Mr. Gould, in America, communicating his acknowledgements of the honour which had been just conferred upon him by the National Academy. On the 2nd of September Mr. Graves went to the observatory, in response to a summons, and the great mathematician at once admitted to his friend that he felt the end was approaching. He mentioned that he had found in the 145th Psalm a wonderfully suitable expression of his thoughts and feelings, and he wished to testify his faith and thankfulness as a Christian by partaking of the Lord's Supper. He died at half-past two on the afternoon of the 2nd of September, 1865, aged sixty years and one month. He was buried in Mount Jerome Cemetery on the 7th of September.

Many were the letters and other more public manifestations of the feelings awakened by Hamilton's death. Sir John Herschel wrote to the widow:—

"Permit me only to add that among the many scientific friends whom time has deprived me of, there has been none whom I more deeply lament, not only for his splendid talents, but for the excellence of his disposition and the perfect simplicity of his manners—so great, and yet devoid of pretensions."

De Morgan, his old mathematical crony, as Hamilton affectionately styled him, also wrote to Lady Hamilton:—

"I have called him one of my dearest friends, and most truly; for I know not how much longer than twenty-five years we have been in intimate correspondence, of most friendly agreement or disagreement, of most cordial interest in each other. And yet we did not know each other's faces. I met him about 1830 at Babbage's breakfast table, and there for the only time in our lives we conversed. I saw him, a long way off, at the dinner given to Herschel (about 1838) on his return from the Cape and there we were not near enough, nor on that crowded day could we get near enough, to exchange a word. And this is all I ever saw, and, so it has pleased God, all I shall see in this world of a man whose friendly communications were among my greatest social enjoyments, and greatest intellectual treats."

There is a very interesting memoir of Hamilton written by De Morgan, in the "Gentleman's Magazine" for 1866, in which he produces an excellent sketch of his friend, illustrated by personal reminiscences and anecdotes. He alludes, among other things, to the picturesque confusion of the papers in his study. There was some sort of order in the mass, discernible however, by Hamilton alone, and any invasion of the domestics, with a view to tidying up, would throw the mathematician as we are informed, into "a good honest thundering passion."

Hardly any two men, who were both powerful mathematicians, could have been more dissimilar in every other respect than were Hamilton and De Morgan. The highly poetical temperament of Hamilton was remarkably contrasted with the practical realism of De Morgan. Hamilton sends sonnets to his friend, who replies by giving the poet advice about making his will. The metaphysical subtleties, with which Hamilton often filled his sheets, did not seem to have the same attraction for De Morgan that he found in battles about the quantification of the Predicate. De Morgan was exquisitely witty, and though his jokes were always appreciated by his correspondent, yet Hamilton seldom ventured on anything of the same kind in reply; indeed his rare attempts at humour only produced results of the most ponderous description. But never were two scientific correspondents more perfectly in sympathy with each other. Hamilton's work on Quaternions, his labours in Dynamics, his literary tastes, his metaphysics, and his poetry, were all heartily welcomed by his friend, whose letters in reply invariably evince the kindliest interest in all Hamilton's concerns. In a similar way De Morgan's letters to Hamilton always met with a heartfelt response.

Alike for the memory of Hamilton, for the credit of his University, and for the benefit of science, let us hope that a collected edition of his works will ere long appear—a collection which shall show those early achievements in splendid optical theory, those achievements of his more mature powers which made him the Lagrange of his country, and finally those creations of the Quaternion Calculus by which new capabilities have been bestowed on the human intellect.

LE VERRIER.

The name of Le Verrier is one that goes down to fame on account of very different discoveries from those which have given renown to several of the other astronomers whom we have mentioned. We are sometimes apt to identify the idea of an astronomer with that of a man who looks through a telescope at the stars; but the word astronomer has really much wider significance. No man who ever lived has been more entitled to be designated an astronomer than Le Verrier, and yet it is certain that he never made a telescopic discovery of any kind. Indeed, so far as his scientific achievements have been concerned, he might never have looked through a telescope at all.

For the full interpretation of the movements of the heavenly bodies, mathematical knowledge of the most advanced character is demanded. The mathematician at the outset calls upon the astronomer who uses the instruments in the observatory, to ascertain for him at various times the exact positions occupied by the sun, the moon, and the planets. These observations, obtained with the greatest care, and purified as far as possible from the errors by which they may be affected form, as it were, the raw material on which the mathematician exercises his skill. It is for him to elicit from the observed places the true laws which govern the movements of the heavenly bodies. Here is indeed a task in which the highest powers of the human intellect may be worthily employed.

Among those who have laboured with the greatest success in the interpretation of the observations made with instruments of precision, Le Verrier holds a highly honoured place. To him it has been given to provide a superb illustration of the success with which the mind of man can penetrate the deep things of Nature.

The illustrious Frenchman, Urban Jean Joseph Le Verrier, was born on the 11th March, 1811, at St. Lo, in the department of Manche. He received his education in that famous school for education in the higher branches of science, the Ecole Polytechnique, and acquired there considerable fame as a mathematician. On leaving the school Le Verrier at first purposed to devote himself to the public service, in the department of civil engineering; and it is worthy of note that his earliest scientific work was not in those mathematical researches in which he was ultimately to become so famous. His duties in the engineering department involved practical chemical research in the laboratory. In this he seems to have become very expert, and probably fame as a chemist would have been thus attained, had not destiny led him into another direction. As it was, he did engage in some original chemical research. His first contributions to science were the fruits of his laboratory work; one of his papers was on the combination of phosphorus and hydrogen, and another on the combination of phosphorus and oxygen.

His mathematical labours at the Ecole Polytechnique had, however, revealed to Le Verrier that he was endowed with the powers requisite for dealing with the subtlest instruments of mathematical analysis. When he was twenty-eight years old, his first great astronomical investigation was brought forth. It will be necessary to enter into some explanation as to the nature of this, inasmuch as it was the commencement of the life-work which he was to pursue.

If but a single planet revolved around the sun, then the orbit of that planet would be an ellipse, and the shape and size, as well as the position of the ellipse, would never alter. One revolution after another would be traced out, exactly in the same manner, in compliance with the force continuously exerted by the sun. Suppose, however, that a second planet be introduced into the system. The sun will exert its attraction on this second planet also, and it will likewise describe an orbit round the central globe. We can, however, no longer assert that the orbit in which either of the planets moves remains exactly an ellipse. We may, indeed, assume that the mass of the sun is enormously greater than that of either of the planets. In this case the attraction of the sun is a force of such preponderating magnitude, that the actual path of each planet remains nearly the same as if the other planet were absent. But it is impossible for the orbit of each planet not to be affected in some degree by the attraction of the other planet. The general law of nature asserts that every body in space attracts every other body. So long as there is only a single planet, it is the single attraction between the sun and that planet which is the sole controlling principle of the movement, and in consequence of it the ellipse is described. But when a second planet is introduced, each of the two bodies is not only subject to the attraction of the sun, but each one of the planets attracts the other. It is true that this mutual attraction is but small, but, nevertheless, it produces some effect. It "disturbs," as the astronomer says, the elliptic orbit which would otherwise have been pursued. Hence it follows that in the actual planetary system where there are several planets disturbing each other, it is not true to say that the orbits are absolutely elliptic.

At the same time in any single revolution a planet may for most practical purposes be said to be actually moving in an ellipse. As, however, time goes on, the ellipse gradually varies. It alters its shape, it alters its plane, and it alters its position in that plane. If, therefore, we want to study the movements of the planets, when great intervals of time are concerned, it is necessary to have the means of learning the nature of the movement of the orbit in consequence of the disturbances it has experienced.

We may illustrate the matter by supposing the planet to be running like a railway engine on a track which has been laid in a long elliptic path. We may suppose that while the planet is coursing along, the shape of the track is gradually altering. But this alteration may be so slow, that it does not appreciably affect the movement of the engine in a single revolution. We can also suppose that the plane in which the rails have been laid has a slow oscillation in level, and that the whole orbit is with more or less uniformity moved slowly about in the plane.

In short periods of time the changes in the shapes and positions of the planetary orbits, in consequence of their mutual attractions, are of no great consequence. When, however, we bring thousands of years into consideration, then the displacements of the planetary orbits attain considerable dimensions, and have, in fact, produced a profound effect on the system.

It is of the utmost interest to investigate the extent to which one planet can affect another in virtue of their mutual attractions. Such investigations demand the exercise of the highest mathematical gifts. But not alone is intellectual ability necessary for success in such inquiries. It must be united with a patient capacity for calculations of an arduous type, protracted, as they frequently have to be, through many years of labour. Le Verrier soon found in these profound inquiries adequate scope for the exercise of his peculiar gifts. His first important astronomical publication contained an investigation of the changes which the orbits of several of the planets, including the earth, have undergone in times past, and which they will undergo in times to come.

As an illustration of these researches, we may take the case of the planet in which we are, of course, especially interested, namely, the earth, and we can investigate the changes which, in the lapse of time, the earth's orbit has undergone, in consequence of the disturbance to which it has been subjected by the other planets. In a century, or even in a thousand years, there is but little recognisable difference in the shape of the track pursued by the earth. Vast periods of time are required for the development of the large consequences of planetary perturbation. Le Verrier has, however, given us the particulars of what the earth's journey through space has been at intervals of 20,000 years back from the present date. His furthest calculation throws our glance back to the state of the earth's track 100,000 years ago, while, with a bound forward, he shows us what the earth's orbit is to be in the future, at successive intervals of 20,000 years, till a date is reached which is 100,000 years in advance of A.D. 1800.

The talent which these researches displayed brought Le Verrier into notice. At that time the Paris Observatory was presided over by Arago, a SAVANT who occupies a distinguished position in French scientific annals. Arago at once perceived that Le Verrier was just the man who possessed the qualifications suitable for undertaking a problem of great importance and difficulty that had begun to force itself on the attention of astronomers. What this great problem was, and how astonishing was the solution it received, must now be considered.

Ever since Herschel brought himself into fame by his superb discovery of the great planet Uranus, the movements of this new addition to the solar system were scrutinized with care and attention. The position of Uranus was thus accurately determined from time to time. At length, when sufficient observations of this remote planet had been brought together, the route which the newly-discovered body pursued through the heavens was ascertained by those calculations with which astronomers are familiar. It happens, however, that Uranus possesses a superficial resemblance to a star. Indeed the resemblance is so often deceptive that long ere its detection as a planet by Herschel, it had been observed time after time by skilful astronomers, who little thought that the star-like point at which they looked was anything but a star. From these early observations it was possible to determine the track of Uranus, and it was found that the great planet takes a period of no less than eighty-four years to accomplish a circuit. Calculations were made of the shape of the orbit in which it revolved before its discovery by Herschel, and these were compared with the orbit which observations showed the same body to pursue in those later years when its planetary character was known. It could not, of course, be expected that the orbit should remain unaltered; the fact that the great planets Jupiter and Saturn revolve in the vicinity of Uranus must necessarily imply that the orbit of the latter undergoes considerable changes. When, however, due allowance has been made for whatever influence the attraction of Jupiter and Saturn, and we may add of the earth and all the other Planets, could possibly produce, the movements of Uranus were still inexplicable. It was perfectly obvious that there must be some other influence at work besides that which could be attributed to the planets already known.

Astronomers could only recognise one solution of such a difficulty. It was impossible to doubt that there must be some other planet in addition to the bodies at that time known, and that the perturbations of Uranus hitherto unaccounted for, were due to the disturbances caused by the action of this unknown planet. Arago urged Le Verrier to undertake the great problem of searching for this body, whose theoretical existence seemed demonstrated. But the conditions of the search were such that it must needs be conducted on principles wholly different from any search which had ever before been undertaken for a celestial object. For this was not a case in which mere survey with a telescope might be expected to lead to the discovery.

Certain facts might be immediately presumed with reference to the unknown object. There could be no doubt that the unknown disturber of Uranus must be a large body with a mass far exceeding that of the earth. It was certain, however, that it must be so distant that it could only appear from our point of view as a very small object. Uranus itself lay beyond the range, or almost beyond the range, of unassisted vision. It could be shown that the planet by which the disturbance was produced revolved in an orbit which must lie outside that of Uranus. It seemed thus certain that the planet could not be a body visible to the unaided eye. Indeed, had it been at all conspicuous its planetary character would doubtless have been detected ages ago. The unknown body must therefore be a planet which would have to be sought for by telescopic aid.

There is, of course, a profound physical difference between a planet and a star, for the star is a luminous sun, and the planet is merely a dark body, rendered visible by the sunlight which falls upon it. Notwithstanding that a star is a sun thousands of times larger than the planet and millions of times more remote, yet it is a singular fact that telescopic planets possess an illusory resemblance to the stars among which their course happens to lie. So far as actual appearance goes, there is indeed only one criterion by which a planet of this kind can be discriminated from a star. If the planet be large enough the telescope will show that it possesses a disc, and has a visible and measurable circular outline. This feature a star does not exhibit. The stars are indeed so remote that no matter how large they may be intrinsically, they only exhibit radiant points of light, which the utmost powers of the telescope fail to magnify into objects with an appreciable diameter. The older and well-known planets, such as Jupiter and Mars, possess discs, which, though not visible to the unaided eye, were clearly enough discernible with the slightest telescopic power. But a very remote planet like Uranus, though it possessed a disc large enough to be quickly appreciated by the consummate observing skill of Herschel, was never-theless so stellar in its appearance, that it had been observed no fewer than seventeen times by experienced astronomers prior to Herschel. In each case the planetary nature of the object had been overlooked, and it had been taken for granted that it was a star. It presented no differ-ence which was sufficient to arrest attention.

As the unknown body by which Uranus was disturbed was cer-tainly much more remote than Uranus, it seemed to be certain that though it might show a disc perceptible to very close inspection, yet that the disc must be so minute as not to be detected except with ex-treme care. In other words, it seemed probable that the body which was to be sought for could not readily be discriminated from a small star, to which class of object it bore a superficial resemblance, though, as a matter of fact, there was the profoundest difference between the two bodies.

There are on the heavens many hundreds of thousands of stars, and the problem of identifying the planet, if indeed it should lie among these stars, seemed a very complex matter. Of course it is the abundant presence of the stars which causes the difficulty. If the stars could have been got rid of, a sweep over the heavens would at once disclose all the planets which are bright enough to be visible with the telescopic power employed. It is the fortuitous resemblance of the planet to the stars which enables it to escape detection. To discriminate the planet among stars everywhere in the sky would be almost impossible. If, however, some method could be devised for localizing that precise region in which the planet's existence might be presumed, then the search could be undertaken with some prospect of success.

To a certain extent the problem of localizing the region on the sky in which the planet might be expected admitted of an immediate limi-tation. It is known that all the planets, or perhaps I ought rather to say, all the great planets, confine their movements to a certain zone around the heavens. This zone extends some way on either side of that line called the ecliptic in which the earth pursues its journey around the sun. It was therefore to be inferred that the new planet need not be sought for outside this zone. It is obvious that this consideration at once reduces the area to be scrutinized to a small fraction of the entire heavens. But even within the zone thus defined there are many thousands of stars. It would seem a hopeless task to detect the new planet unless some further limitation to its position could be assigned.

It was accordingly suggested to Le Verrier that he should endeavour to discover in what particular part of the strip of the celestial sphere which we have indicated the search for the unknown planet should be instituted. The materials available to the mathematician for the solution of this problem were to be derived solely from the discrepancies between the calculated places in which Uranus should be found, taking into account the known causes of disturbance, and the actual places in which observation had shown the planet to exist. Here was indeed an unprecedented problem, and one of extraordinary difficulty. Le Verrier, however, faced it, and, to the astonishment of the world, succeeded in carrying it through to a brilliant solution. We cannot here attempt to enter into any account of the mathematical investigations that were necessary. All that we can do is to give a general indication of the method which had to be adopted.

Let us suppose that a planet is revolving outside Uranus, at a distance which is suggested by the several distances at which the other planets are dispersed around the sun. Let us assume that this outer planet has started on its course, in a prescribed path, and that it has a certain mass. It will, of course, disturb the motion of Uranus, and in consequence of that disturbance Uranus will follow a path the nature of which can be determined by calculation. It will, however, generally be found that the path so ascertained does not tally with the actual path which observations have indicated for Uranus. This demonstrates that the assumed circumstances of the unknown planet must be in some respects erroneous, and the astronomer commences afresh with an amended orbit. At last after many trials, Le Verrier ascertained that, by assuming a certain size, shape, and position for the unknown Planet's orbit, and a certain value for the mass of the hypothetical body, it would be possible to account for the observed disturbances of Uranus. Gradually it became clear to the perception of this consummate mathematician, not only that the difficulties in the movements of Uranus could be thus explained, but that no other explanation need be sought for. It accordingly appeared that a planet possessing the mass which he had assigned, and moving in the orbit which his calculations had indicated, must indeed exist, though no eye had ever beheld any such body. Here was, indeed, an astonishing result. The mathematician sitting at his desk, by studying the observations which had been supplied to him of one planet, is able to discover the existence of another planet, and even to assign the very position which it must occupy, ere ever the telescope is invoked for its discovery.

Thus it was that the calculations of Le Verrier narrowed greatly the area to be scrutinised in the telescopic search which was presently to be instituted. It was already known, as we have just pointed out, that the planet must lie somewhere on the ecliptic. The French mathematician had now further indicated the spot on the ecliptic at which, according to his calculations, the planet must actually be found. And now for an episode in this history which will be celebrated so long as science shall endure. It is nothing less than the telescopic confirmation of the existence of this new planet, which had previously been indicated only by mathematical calculation. Le Verrier had not himself the instruments necessary for studying the heavens, nor did he possess the skill of the practical astronomer. He, therefore, wrote to Dr. Galle, of the Observatory at Berlin, requesting him to undertake a telescopic search for the new planet in the vicinity which the mathematical calculation had indicated for the whereabouts of the planet at that particular time. Le Verrier added that he thought the planet ought to admit of being recognised by the possession of a disc sufficiently definite to mark the distinction between it and the surrounding stars.

It was the 23rd September, 1846, when the request from Le Verrier reached the Berlin Observatory, and the night was clear, so that the memorable search was made on the same evening. The investigation was facilitated by the circumstance that a diligent observer had recently compiled elaborate star maps for certain tracts of the heavens lying in a sufficiently wide zone on both sides of the equator. These maps were as yet only partially complete, but it happened that Hora. XXI., which included the very spot which Le Verrier's results referred to, had been just issued. Dr. Galle had thus before his, eyes a chart of all the stars which were visible in that part of the heavens at the time when the map was made. The advantage of such an assistance to the search could hardly be over-estimated. It at once gave the astronomer another method of recognising the planet besides that afforded by its possible possession of a disc. For as the planet was a moving body, it would not have been in the same place relatively to the stars at the time when the map was constructed, as it occupied some years later when the search was being made. If the body should be situated in the spot which Le Verrier's calculations indicated in the autumn of 1846, then it might be regarded as certain that it would not be found in that same place on a map drawn some years previously.

The search to be undertaken consisted in a comparison made point by point between the bodies shown on the map, and those stars in the sky which Dr. Galle's telescope revealed. In the course of this comparison it presently appeared that a star-like object of the eighth magnitude, which was quite a conspicuous body in the telescope, was not represented in the map. This at once attracted the earnest attention of the astronomer, and raised his hopes that here was indeed the planet. Nor were these hopes destined to be disappointed. It could not be supposed that a star of the eighth magnitude would have been overlooked in the preparation of a chart whereon stars of many lower degrees of brightness were set down. One other supposition was of course conceivable. It might have been that this suspicious object belonged to the class of variables, for there are many such stars whose brightness fluctuates, and if it had happened that the map was constructed at a time when the star in question had but feeble brilliance, it might have escaped notice. It is also well known that sometimes new stars suddenly develop, so that the possibility that what Dr. Galle saw should have been a variable star or should have been a totally new star had to be provided against.

Fortunately a test was immediately available to decide whether the new object was indeed the long sought for planet, or whether it was a star of one of the two classes to which I have just referred. A star remains fixed, but a planet is in motion. No doubt when a planet lies at the distance at which this new planet was believed to be situated, its apparent motion would be so slow that it would not be easy to detect any change in the course of a single night's observation. Dr. Galle, however, addressed himself with much skill to the examination of the place of the new body. Even in the course of the night he thought he detected slight movements, and he awaited with much anxiety the renewal of his observations on the subsequent evenings. His suspicions as to the movement of the body were then amply confirmed, and the planetary nature of the new object was thus unmistakably detected.

Great indeed was the admiration of the scientific world at this superb triumph. Here was a mighty planet whose very existence was revealed by the indications afforded by refined mathematical calculation. At once the name of Le Verrier, already known to those conversant with the more profound branches of astronomy, became everywhere celebrated. It soon, however, appeared, that the fame belonging to this great achievement had to be shared between Le Verrier and another astronomer, J. C. Adams, of Cambridge. In our chapter on this great English mathematician we shall describe the manner in which he was independently led to the same discovery.

Directly the planetary nature of the newly-discovered body had been established, the great observatories naturally included this additional member of the solar system in their working lists, so that day after day its place was carefully determined. When sufficient time had elapsed the shape and position of the orbit of the body became known. Of course, it need hardly be said that observations applied to the planet itself must necessarily provide a far more accurate method of determining the path which it follows, than would be possible to Le Verrier, when all he had to base his calculations upon was the influence of the planet reflected, so to speak, from Uranus. It may be noted that the true elements of the planet, when revealed by direct observation, showed that there was a considerable discrepancy between the track of the planet which Le Verrier had announced, and that which the planet was actually found to pursue.

The name of the newly-discovered body had next to be considered. As the older members of the system were already known by the same names as great heathen divinities, it was obvious that some similar source should be invoked for a suggestion as to a name for the most recent planet. The fact that this body was so remote in the depths of space, not unnaturally suggested the name "Neptune." Such is accordingly the accepted designation of that mighty globe which revolves in the track that at present seems to trace out the frontiers of our system.

Le Verrier attained so much fame by this discovery, that when, in 1854, Arago's place had to be filled at the head of the great Paris Observatory, it was universally felt that the discoverer of Neptune was the suitable man to assume the office which corresponds in France to that of the Astronomer Royal in England. It was true that the work of the astronomical mathematician had hitherto been of an abstract character. His discoveries had been made at his desk and not in the observatory, and he had no practical acquaintance with the use of astronomical instruments. However, he threw himself into the technical duties of the observatory with vigour and determination. He endeavoured to inspire the officers of the establishment with enthusiasm for that systematic work which is so necessary for the accomplishment of useful astronomical research. It must, however, be admitted that Le Verrier was not gifted with those natural qualities which would make him adapted for the successful administration of such an establishment. Unfortunately disputes arose between the Director and his staff. At last the difficulties of the situation became so great that the only possible solution was to supersede Le Verrier, and he was accordingly obliged to retire. He was succeeded in his high office by another eminent mathematician, M. Delaunay, only less distinguished than Le Verrier himself.

Relieved of his official duties, Le Verrier returned to the mathematics he loved. In his non-official capacity he continued to work with the greatest ardour at his researches on the movements of the planets. After the death of M. Delaunay, who was accidentally drowned in 1873, Le Verrier was restored to the directorship of the observatory, and he continued to hold the office until his death.

The nature of the researches to which the life of Le Verrier was subsequently devoted are not such as admit of description in a general sketch like this, where the language, and still less the symbols, of mathematics could not be suitably introduced. It may, however, be said in general that he was particularly engaged with the study of the effects produced on the movements of the planets by their mutual attractions. The importance of this work to astronomy consists, to a considerable extent, in the fact that by such calculations we are enabled to prepare tables by which the places of the different heavenly bodies can be predicted for our almanacs. To this task Le Verrier devoted himself, and the amount of work he has accomplished would perhaps have been deemed impossible had it not been actually done.

The superb success which had attended Le Verrier's efforts to explain the cause of the perturbations of Uranus, naturally led this wonderful computer to look for a similar explanation of certain other irregularities in planetary movements. To a large extent he succeeded in showing how the movements of each of the great planets could be satisfactorily accounted for by the influence of the attractions of the other bodies of the same class. One circumstance in connection with these investigations is sufficiently noteworthy to require a few words here. Just as at the opening of his career, Le Verrier had discovered that Uranus, the outermost planet of the then known system, exhibited the influence of an unknown external body, so now it appeared to him that Mercury, the innermost body of our system, was also subjected to some disturbances, which could not be satisfactorily accounted for as consequences of any known agents of attraction. The ellipse in which Mercury revolved was animated by a slow movement, which caused it to revolve in its plane. It appeared to Le Verrier that this displacement was incapable of explanation by the action of any of the known bodies of our system. He was, therefore, induced to try whether he could not determine from the disturbances of Mercury the existence of some other planet, at present unknown, which revolved inside the orbit of the known planet. Theory seemed to indicate that the observed alteration in the track of the planet could be thus accounted for. He naturally desired to obtain telescopic confirmation which might verify the existence of such a body in the same way as Dr. Galle verified the existence of Neptune. If there were, indeed, an intramercurial planet, then it must occasionally cross between the earth and the sun, and might now and then be expected to be witnessed in the actual act of transit. So confident did Le Verrier feel in the existence of such a body that an observation of a dark object in transit, by Lescarbault on 26th March, 1859, was believed by the mathematician to be the object which his theory indicated. Le Verrier also thought it likely that another transit of the same object would be seen in March, 1877. Nothing of the kind was, however, witnessed, notwithstanding that an assiduous watch was kept, and the explanation of the change in Mercury's orbit must, therefore, be regarded as still to be sought for.

Le Verrier naturally received every honour that could be bestowed upon a man of science. The latter part of his life was passed during the most troubled period of modern French history. He was a supporter of the Imperial Dynasty, and during the Commune he experienced much anxiety; indeed, at one time grave fears were entertained for his personal safety.

Early in 1877 his health, which had been gradually failing for some years, began to give way. He appeared to rally somewhat in the summer, but in September he sank rapidly, and died on Sunday, the 23rd of that month.

His remains were borne to the cemetery on Mont Parnasse in a public funeral. Among his pallbearers were leading men of science, from other countries as well as France, and the memorial discourses pronounced at the grave expressed their admiration of his talents and of the greatness of the services he had rendered to science.

ADAMS.

The illustrious mathematician who, among Englishmen, at all events, was second only to Newton by his discoveries in theoretical astronomy, was born on June the 5th, 1819, at the farmhouse of Lidcot, seven miles from Launceston, in Cornwall. His early education was imparted under the guidance of the Rev. John Couch Grylls, a first cousin of his mother. He appears to have received an education of the ordinary school type in classics and mathematics, but his leisure hours were largely devoted to studying what astronomical books he could find in the library of the Mechanics' Institute at Devonport. He was twenty years old when he entered St. John's College, Cambridge. His career in the University was one of almost unparalleled distinction, and it is recorded that his answering at the Wranglership examination, where he came out at the head of the list in 1843, was so high that he received more than double the marks awarded to the Second Wrangler.

Among the papers found after his death was the following memorandum, dated July the 3rd, 1841: "Formed a design at the beginning of this week of investigating, as soon as possible after taking my degree, the irregularities in the motion of Uranus, which are as yet unaccounted for, in order to find whether they may be attributed to the action of an undiscovered planet beyond it; and, if possible, thence to determine the elements of its orbit approximately, which would lead probably to its discovery."

After he had taken his degree, and had thus obtained a little relaxation from the lines within which his studies had previously been necessarily confined, Adams devoted himself to the study of the perturbations of Uranus, in accordance with the resolve which we have

JOHN COUCH ADAMS.

just seen that he formed while he was still an undergraduate. As a first attempt he made the supposition that there might be a planet exterior to Uranus, at a distance which was double that of Uranus from the sun. Having completed his calculation as to the effect which such a hypothetical planet might exercise upon the movement of Uranus, he came to the conclusion that it would be quite possible to account completely for the unexplained difficulties by the action of an exterior planet, if only that planet were of adequate size and had its orbit properly placed. It was necessary, however, to follow up the problem more precisely, and accordingly an application was made through Professor Challis, the Director of the Cambridge Observatory, to the Astronomer Royal, with the object of obtaining from the observations made at Greenwich Observatory more accurate values for the disturbances suffered by Uranus. Basing his work on the more precise materials thus available, Adams undertook his calculations anew, and at last, with his completed results, he called at Greenwich Observatory on October the 21st, 1845. He there left for the Astronomer Royal a paper which contained the results at which he had arrived for the mass and the mean distance of the hypothetical planet as well as the other elements necessary for calculating its exact position.

As we have seen in the preceding chapter, Le Verrier had been also investigating the same problem. The place which Le Verrier assigned to the hypothetical disturbing planet for the beginning of the year 1847, was within a degree of that to which Adams's computations pointed, and which he had communicated to the Astronomer Royal seven months before Le Verrier's work appeared. On July the 29th, 1846, Professor Challis commenced to search for the unknown object with the North-umberland telescope belonging to the Cambridge Observatory. He confined his attention to a limited region in the heavens, extending around that point to which Mr. Adams' calculations pointed. The relative places of all the stars, or rather star-like objects within this area, were to be carefully measured. When the same observations were repeated a week or two later, then the distances of the several pairs of stars from each other would be found unaltered, but any planet which happened to lie among the objects measured would disclose its existence by the alterations in distance due to its motion in the interval. This method of search, though no doubt it must ultimately have proved successful, was necessarily a very tedious one, but to Professor Challis, unfortunately, no other method was available. Thus it happened that, though Challis commenced his search at Cambridge two months earlier than Galle at Berlin, yet, as we have already explained, the possession of accurate star-maps by Dr. Galle enabled him to discover the planet on the very first night that he looked for it.

The rival claims of Adams and Le Verrier to the discovery of Neptune, or rather, we should say, the claims put forward by their respective champions, for neither of the illustrious investigators themselves condescended to enter into the personal aspect of the question, need not be further discussed here. The main points of the controversy have been long since settled, and we cannot do better than quote the words of Sir John Herschel when he addressed the Royal Astronomical Society in 1848:—

"As genius and destiny have joined the names of Le Verrier and Adams, I shall by no means put them asunder; nor will they ever be pronounced apart so long as language shall celebrate the triumphs of science in her sublimest walks. On the great discovery of Neptune, which may be said to have surpassed, by intelligible and legitimate means, the wildest pretensions of clairvoyance, it Would now be quite superfluous for me to dilate. That glorious event and the steps which led to it, and the various lights in which it has been placed, are already familiar to every one having the least tincture of science. I will only add that as there is not, nor henceforth ever can be, the slightest rivalry on the subject between these two illustrious men—as they have met as brothers, and as such will, I trust, ever regard each other—we have made, we could make, no distinction between then, on this occasion. May they both long adorn and augment our science, and add to their own fame already so high and pure, by fresh achievements."

Adams was elected a Fellow of St. John's College, Cambridge, in 1843; but as he did not take holy orders, his Fellowship, in accordance with the rules then existing came to an end in 1852. In the following year he was, however, elected to a Fellowship at Pembroke College, which he retained until the end of his life. In 1858 he was appointed Professor of Mathematics in the University of St. Andrews, but his residence in the north was only a brief one, for in the same year he was recalled to Cambridge as Lowndean Professor of Astronomy and Geometry, in succession to Peacock. In 1861 Challis retired from the Directorship of the Cambridge Observatory, and Adams was appointed to succeed him.

The discovery of Neptune was a brilliant inauguration of the astronomical career of Adams. He worked at, and wrote upon, the theory of the motions of Biela's comet; he made important corrections to the theory of Saturn; he investigated the mass of Uranus, a subject in which he was naturally interested from its importance in the theory of Neptune; he also improved the methods of computing the orbits of double stars. But all these must be regarded as his minor labours, for next to the discovery of Neptune the fame of Adams mainly rests on his researches upon certain movements of the moon, and upon the November meteors.

The periodic time of the moon is the interval required for one circuit of its orbit. This interval is known with accuracy at the present day, and by means of the ancient eclipses the period of the moon's revolution two thousand years ago can be also ascertained. It had been discovered by Halley that the period which the moon requires to accomplish each of its revolutions around the earth has been steadily, though no doubt slowly, diminishing. The change thus produced is not appreciable when only small intervals of time are considered, but it becomes appreciable when we have to deal with intervals of thousands of years. The actual effect which is produced by the lunar acceleration, for so this phenomenon is called, may be thus estimated. If we suppose that the moon had, throughout the ages, revolved around the earth in precisely the same periodic time which it has at present, and if from this assumption we calculate back to find where the moon must have been about two thousand years ago, we obtain a position which the ancient eclipses show to be different from that in which the moon was actually situated. The interval between the position in which the moon would have been found two thousand years ago if there had been no acceleration, and the position in which the moon was actually placed, amounts to about a degree, that is to say, to an arc on the heavens which is twice the moon's apparent diameter.

If no other bodies save the earth and the moon were present in the universe, it seems certain that the motion of the moon would never have exhibited this acceleration. In such a simple case as that which I have supposed the orbit of the moon would have remained for ever absolutely unchanged. It is, however, well known that the presence of the sun exerts a disturbing influence upon the movements of the moon. In each revolution our satellite is continually drawn aside by the action of the sun from the place which it would otherwise have occupied. These irregularities are known as the perturbations of the lunar orbit, they have long been studied, and the majority of them have been satisfactorily accounted for. It seems, however, to those who first investigated the question that the phenomenon of the lunar acceleration could not be explained as a consequence of solar perturbation, and, as no other agent competent to produce such effects was recognised by astronomers, the lunar acceleration presented an unsolved enigma.

At the end of the last century the illustrious French mathematician Laplace undertook a new investigation of the famous problem, and was rewarded with a success which for a long time appeared to be quite complete. Let us suppose that the moon lies directly between the earth and the sun, then both earth and moon are pulled towards the sun by the solar attraction; as, however, the moon is the nearer of the two bodies to the attracting centre it is pulled the more energetically, and consequently there is an increase in the distance between the earth and the moon. Similarly when the moon happens to lie on the other side of the earth, so that the earth is interposed directly between the moon and the sun, the solar attraction exerted upon the earth is more powerful than the same influence upon the moon. Consequently in this case, also, the distance of the moon from the earth is increased by the solar disturbance. These instances will illustrate the general truth, that, as one of the consequences of the disturbing influence exerted by the sun upon the earth-moon system, there is an increase in the dimensions of the average orbit which the moon describes around the earth. As the time required by the moon to accomplish a journey round the earth depends upon its distance from the earth, it follows that among the influences of the sun upon the moon there must be an enlargement of the periodic time, from what it would have been had there been no solar disturbing action.

This was known long before the time of Laplace, but it did not directly convey any explanation of the lunar acceleration. It no doubt amounted to the assertion that the moon's periodic time was slightly augmented by the disturbance, but it did not give any grounds for suspecting that there was a continuous change in progress. It was, however, apparent that the periodic time was connected with the solar disturbance, so that, if there were any alteration in the amount of the sun's disturbing effect, there must be a corresponding alteration in the moon's periodic time. Laplace, therefore, perceived that, if he could discover any continuous change in the ability of the sun for disturbing the moon, he would then have accounted for a continuous change in the moon's periodic time, and that thus an explanation of the long-vexed question of the lunar acceleration might be forthcoming.

The capability of the sun for disturbing the earth-moon system is obviously connected with the distance of the earth from the sun. If the earth moved in an orbit which underwent no change whatever, then the efficiency of the sun as a disturbing agent would not undergo any change of the kind which was sought for. But if there were any alteration in the shape or size of the earth's orbit, then that might involve such changes in the distance between the earth and the sun as would possibly afford the desired agent for producing the observed lunar effect. It is known that the earth revolves in an orbit which, though nearly circular, is strictly an ellipse. If the earth were the only planet revolving around the sun then that ellipse would remain unaltered from age to age. The earth is, however, only one of a large number of planets which circulate around the great luminary, and are guided and controlled by his supreme attracting power. These planets mutually attract each other, and in consequence of their mutual attractions the orbits of the planets are disturbed from the simple elliptic form which they would otherwise possess. The movement of the earth, for instance, is not, strictly speaking, performed in an elliptical orbit. We may, however, regard it as revolving in an ellipse provided we admit that the ellipse is itself in slow motion.

It is a remarkable characteristic of the disturbing effects of the planets that the ellipse in which the earth is at any moment moving always retains the same length; that is to say, its longest diameter is invariable. In all other respects the ellipse is continually changing. It alters its position, it changes its plane, and, most important of all, it changes its eccentricity. Thus, from age to age the shape of the track which the earth describes may at one time be growing more nearly a circle, or at another time may be departing more widely from a circle. These alterations are very small in amount, and they take place with extreme slowness, but they are in incessant progress, and their amount admits of being accurately calculated. At the present time, and for thousands of years past, as well as for thousands of years to come, the eccentricity of the earth's orbit is diminishing, and consequently the orbit described by the earth each year is becoming more nearly circular. We must, however, remember that under all circumstances the length of the longest axis of the ellipse is unaltered, and consequently the size of the track which the earth describes around the sun is gradually increasing. In other words, it may be said that during the present ages the average distance between the earth and the sun is waxing greater in consequence of the perturbations which the earth experiences from the attraction of the other planets. We have, however, already seen that the efficiency of the solar attraction for disturbing the moon's movement depends on the distance between the earth and the sun. As therefore the average distance between the earth and the sun is increasing, at all events during the thousands of years over which our observations extend, it follows that the ability of the sun for disturbing the moon must be gradually diminishing.

It has been pointed out that, in consequence of the solar disturbance, the orbit of the moon must be some what enlarged. As it now appears that the solar disturbance is on the whole declining, it follows that the orbit of the moon, which has to be adjusted relatively to the average value of the solar disturbance, must also be gradually declining. In other words, the moon must be approaching nearer to the earth in consequence of the alterations in the eccentricity of the earth's orbit produced by the attraction of the other planets. It is true that the change in the moon's position thus arising is an extremely small one, and the consequent effect in accelerating the moon's motion is but very slight. It is in fact almost imperceptible, except when great periods of time are involved. Laplace undertook a calculation on this subject. He knew what the efficiency of the planets in altering the dimensions of the earth's orbit amounted to; from this he was able to determine the changes that would be propagated into the motion of the moon. Thus he ascertained, or at all events thought he had ascertained, that the acceleration of the moon's motion, as it had been inferred from the observations of the ancient eclipses which have been handed down to us, could be completely accounted for as a consequence of planetary perturbation. This was regarded as a great scientific triumph. Our be-

CAMBRIDGE OBSERVATORY

lief in the universality of the law of gravitation would, in fact, have been seriously challenged unless some explanation of the lunar acceleration had been forthcoming. For about fifty years no one questioned the truth of Laplace's investigation. When a mathematician of his eminence had rendered an explanation of the remarkable facts of observation which seemed so complete, it is not surprising that there should have been but little temptation to doubt it. On undertaking a new calculation of the same question, Professor Adams found that Laplace had not pursued this approximation sufficiently far, and that consequently there was a considerable error in the result of his analysis. Adams, it must be observed, did not impugn the value of the lunar acceleration which Halley had deduced from the observations, but what he did show was, that the calculation by which Laplace thought he had provided an explanation of this acceleration was erroneous. Adams, in fact, proved that the planetary influence which Laplace had detected only possessed about half the efficiency which the great French mathematician had attributed to it. There were not wanting illustrious mathematicians who came forward to defend the calculations of Laplace. They computed the question anew and arrived at results practically coincident with those he had given. On the other hand certain distinguished mathematicians at home and abroad verified the results of Adams. The issue was merely a mathematical one. It had only one correct solution. Gradually it appeared that those who opposed Adams presented a number of different solutions, all of them discordant with his, and, usually, discordant with each other. Adams showed distinctly where each of these investigators had fallen into error, and at last it became universally admitted that the Cambridge Professor had corrected Laplace in a very fundamental point of astronomical theory.

Though it was desirable to have learned the truth, yet the breach between observation and calculation which Laplace was believed to have closed thus became reopened. Laplace's investigation, had it been correct, would have exactly explained the observed facts. It was, however, now shown that his solution was not correct, and that the lunar acceleration, when strictly calculated as a consequence of solar perturbations, only produced about half the effect which was wanted to explain the ancient eclipses completely. It now seems certain that there is no means of accounting for the lunar acceleration as a direct consequence of the laws of gravitation, if we suppose, as we have been in the habit of supposing, that the members of the solar system concerned may be regarded as rigid particles. It has, however, been suggested that another explanation of a very interesting kind may be forthcoming, and this we must endeavour to set forth.

It will be remembered that we have to explain why the period of revolution of the moon is now shorter than it used to be. If we imagine the length of the period to be expressed in terms of days and fractions of a day, that is to say, in terms of the rotations of the earth around its axis, then the difficulty encountered is, that the moon now requires for each of its revolutions around the earth rather a smaller number of rotations of the earth around its axis than used formerly to be the case. Of course this may be explained by the fact that the moon is now moving more swiftly than of yore, but it is obvious that an explanation of quite a different kind might be conceivable. The moon may be moving just at the same pace as ever, but the length of the day may be increasing. If the length of the day is increasing, then, of course, a smaller number of days will be required for the moon to perform each revolution even though the moon's period was itself really unchanged. It would, therefore, seem as if the phenomenon known as the lunar acceleration is the result of the two causes. The first of these is that discovered by Laplace, though its value was over-estimated by him, in which the perturbations of the earth by the planets indirectly affect the motion of the moon. The remaining part of the acceleration of our satellite is apparent rather than real, it is not that the moon is moving more quickly, but that our time-piece, the earth, is revolving more slowly, and is thus actually losing time. It is interesting to note that we can detect a physical explanation for the apparent checking of the earth's motion which is thus manifested. The tides which ebb and flow on the earth exert a brake-like action on the revolving globe, and there can be no doubt that they are gradually reducing its speed, and thus lengthening the day. It has accordingly been suggested that it is this action of the tides which produces the supplementary effect necessary to complete the physical explanation of the lunar acceleration, though it would perhaps be a little premature to assert that this has been fully demonstrated.

The third of Professor Adams' most notable achievements was connected with the great shower of November meteors which astonished the world in 1866. This splendid display concentrated the attention of astronomers on the theory of the movements of the little objects by which the display was produced. For the definite discovery of the track in which these bodies revolve, we are indebted to the labours of Professor Adams, who, by a brilliant piece of mathematical work, completed the edifice whose foundations had been laid by Professor Newton, of Yale, and other astronomers.

Meteors revolve around the sun in a vast swarm, every individual member of which pursues an orbit in accordance with the well-known laws of Kepler. In order to understand the movements of these objects, to account satisfactorily for their periodic recurrence, and to predict the times of their appearance, it became necessary to learn the size and the shape of the track which the swarm followed, as well as the position which it occupied. Certain features of the track could no doubt be readily assigned. The fact that the shower recurs on one particular day of the year, viz., November 13th, defines one point through which the orbit must pass. The position on the heavens of the radiant point from which the meteors appear to diverge, gives another element in the track. The sun must of course be situated at the focus, so that only one further piece of information, namely, the periodic time, will be necessary to complete our knowledge of the movements of the system. Professor H. Newton, of Yale, had shown that the choice of possible orbits for the meteoric swarm is limited to five. There is, first, the great ellipse in which we now know the meteors revolve once every thirty three and one quarter years. There is next an orbit of a nearly circular kind in which the periodic time would be a little more than a year. There is a similar track in which the periodic time would be a few days short of a year, while two other smaller orbits would also be conceivable. Professor Newton had pointed out a test by which it would be possible to select the true orbit, which we know must be one or other of these five. The mathematical difficulties which attended the application of this test were no doubt great, but they did not baffle Professor Adams.

There is a continuous advance in the date of this meteoric shower. The meteors now cross our track at the point occupied by the earth on November 13th, but this point is gradually altering. The only influence known to us which could account for the continuous change in the plane of the meteor's orbit arises from the attraction of the various planets. The problem to be solved may therefore be attacked in this manner. A specified amount of change in the plane of the orbit of the meteors is known to arise, and the changes which ought to result from the attraction of the planets can be computed for each of the five possible orbits, in one of which it is certain that the meteors must revolve. Professor Adams undertook the work. Its difficulty principally arises from the high eccentricity of the largest of the orbits, which renders the more ordinary methods of calculation inapplicable. After some months of arduous labour the work was completed, and in April, 1867, Adams announced his solution of the problem. He showed that if the meteors revolved in the largest of the five orbits, with the periodic time of thirty three and one quarter years, the perturbations of Jupiter would account for a change to the extent of twenty minutes of arc in the point in which the orbit crosses the earth's track. The attraction of Saturn would augment this by seven minutes, and Uranus would add one minute more, while the influence of the Earth and of the other planets would be inappreciable. The accumulated effect is thus twenty-eight minutes, which is practically coincident with the observed value as determined by Professor Newton from an examination of all the showers of which there is any historical record. Having thus showed that the great orbit was a possible path for the meteors, Adams next proved that no one of the other four orbits would be disturbed in the same manner. Indeed, it appeared that not half the observed amount of change could arise in any orbit except in that one with the long period. Thus was brought to completion the interesting research which demonstrated the true relation of the meteor swarm to the solar system.

Besides those memorable scientific labours with which his attention was so largely engaged, Professor Adams found time for much other study. He occasionally allowed himself to undertake as a relaxation some pieces of numerical calculation, so tremendously long that we can only look on them with astonishment. He has calculated certain important mathematical constants accurately to more than two hundred places of decimals. He was a diligent reader of works on history, geology, and botany, and his arduous labours were often beguiled by novels, of which, like many other great men, he was very fond. He had also the taste of a collector, and he brought together about eight hundred volumes of early printed works, many of considerable rarity and value. As to his personal character, I may quote the words of Dr. Glaisher when he says, "Strangers who first met him were invariably struck by his simple and unaffected manner. He was a delightful companion, always cheerful and genial, showing in society but few traces of his really shy and retiring disposition. His nature was sympathetic and generous, and in few men have the moral and intellectual qualities been more perfectly balanced."

In 1863 he married the daughter of Haliday Bruce, Esq., of Dublin and up to the close of his life he lived at the Cambridge Observatory, pursuing his mathematical work and enjoying the society of his friends.

He died, after a long illness, on 21st January, 1892, and was interred in St. Giles's Cemetery, on the Huntingdon Road, Cambridge.

Made in United States
Orlando, FL
01 August 2023

35667844R00168